D1432447

THEIR MAJESTIES' ASTRONOMERS

Their Majesties' Astronomers

A survey of astronomy in Britain between the two Elizabeths

COLIN A. RONAN

THE BODLEY HEAD

LONDON   SYDNEY
TORONTO

© Colin Ronan 1967
Printed and bound in Great Britain for
The Bodley Head Ltd
9 Bow Street, London, wc2
by C. Tinling & Co Ltd, Prescot
Set in Linotype Garamond
First published 1967

TO
ANN

Preface

Astronomy, like all science, is international: nowhere in the world is there an observatory or a research institute that can pursue its work in glorious isolation. Any attempt to work alone, without the stimulation of other views and ideas, is likely to be ineffective. Yet this does not mean that science is stateless; like other creative activities, it is flavoured by the character of the men and women who pursue it. In any international project, national characteristics keep appearing, fortunately not as petty nationalism but rather as a bias in outlook. There are nearly as many ways of tackling a problem as there are people to do it, and if any excuse is needed for sketching the development of astronomy in Britain, it is that to do so allows us to appreciate the unique contributions that have been made by British astronomers over the last four centuries. Today, when giant radio telescopes are becoming commonplace, astronomy has become 'big science' with an expensive budget, and this even in a country that is not trying to land men on the Moon or send space probes to Mars and beyond. The taxpayer is being asked to contribute money for research in what has always seemed to be a rather esoteric science, with little if any immediate practical applications. Why he should agree—indeed, why he should be enthusiastic about it—will only become clear if we can see modern research against the backcloth of previous achievement. But the story of British astronomy is worth telling in its own right, partly because of the personalities involved and partly because we so often forget our heritage in the desire to honour others.

This book can, however, do no more than provide an outline of what has been achieved; many names and details have had to be omitted not because of any unworthiness but purely because to include them would require a series of volumes. All the same it is hoped that it will at least show the two types of astronomer who have brought us to our mid-twentieth-century view of the universe: the theoretician and the practical observer. The contrasts between the chapters may show their essential differences: on the one hand we see the hard, often uneventful work of the observer who has pursued the holy grail of accuracy, and on the other we witness the broad sweep of the theoretical astronomer who gathers the entire universe of space and time into his philosophical net.

I have also attempted the dangerous task of trying to assess in brief the way astronomy and astronomers seem to be going at the present time. This can be invidious when it comes to mentioning names and painting a picture of the contemporary era which is still too close to permit of true historical perspective. Yet it is important to make the attempt, since astronomy is at a most exciting and vital stage of its development: we stand now on the brink of a new revolution in knowledge and can only neglect it at our peril. The British astronomer, like his colleagues abroad, is helping to bring about this revolution and it would be wrong to omit all mention of it.

Many people have helped in providing information for this book, but my thanks are especially due to Mr Patrick Moore for details of the history of Armagh Observatory; to Mr N. G Matthew for facts about the Royal Observatory, Edinburgh; and to Mr William Christie for personal and other details of his grandfather, the eighth Astronomer Royal, and for generously permitting me to look at private papers in his possession. To my wife I owe a great debt, for not only has she made useful suggestions about illustrations and helped me to iron out many inconsistencies and inelegancies in the text, but she has also typed a manuscript that has kept her too long from her own work.

Colin A. Ronan

Contents

Illustrations

I

Perspective

THE BEGINNINGS of astronomy can be traced back some five thousand years, to the early days of the Egyptian and Mesopotamian civilisations, but in Britain there was no science of the heavens before the Renaissance. The tribes that made up the population no doubt had a primitive star lore of their own, yet there is no evidence that this could be dignified by the name of science. As far as Britain is concerned, the scientific study of the sky is a comparatively recent development, and seems to have begun in earnest no earlier than Elizabethan times—a mere four hundred years ago. Certainly there had been adventurous spirits like Adelard of Bath (*fl.* 1126) and Robert of Chester (*fl.* 1145), who went to Spain and learned Arabic in order to translate Arabic versions of Greek scientific books into Latin and thus make them available to other scholars of western Christendom. Yet vitally necessary though it was to make use of the vast store of scientific knowledge that the Greeks had amassed over some seven and a half centuries, in Britain this was not done and there was no independent astronomical research. Independent thinking only began when two important factors coincided —the expansion of the first Elizabethan era and the arrival of a revolutionary astronomical theory from Poland.

Astronomy before the mid-sixteenth century was parochial compared with the vast expanses of space that astronomers were to probe after the telescope was invented. The stars were merely guides, and were thought of as fixed to the inside of a giant sphere of the heavens. They formed a pattern that the astronomer could read like a map. It was a map with fanciful contours, for the stars were grouped into constellations depicting animals or legends handed down almost unchanged from the Minoan civilisation of the third millenium B.C., but nonetheless it was a map. No one enquired about the nature of the stars. They seemed to be spherical in shape, fixed in position, and eternal in existence, while they were certainly inaccessible. They were seen purely as a background against which the movements of a few other celestial bodies could be charted, and it was the Sun, Moon and planets that captured the imagination and riveted the astronomer's attention. Admittedly the signs of the zodiac—those constellations like Taurus, Gemini and Pisces, through which the planets, Sun and Moon travelled—were considered important, but this was because of their supposed effects on the lives of human beings, not because of any curiosity about their real nature. The pseudo-science of astrology was accepted by most people, lettered or unlettered, and it was merely the astral influences thought to emanate from the zodiacal signs that rendered them more significant than the other constellations. However, we must be careful here, for astrology acted as an important stimulant to astronomers. It provided them with the patronage that enabled them to make their observations and was often the sole *raison d'être* behind the careful examination of planetary motions; and, as such, it had a beneficial effect on the science of astronomy. Only after the mid-seventeenth century was knowledge sufficient to cast astrology into the limbo of mistaken beliefs and discredited superstitions, and it is only with the growing popular knowledge of science in the last hundred years that it has become almost a pernicious folly.

At all events, the real task of the astronomer was to account precisely for the behaviour of the Sun, Moon and planets with a degree of accuracy sufficient to allow him to compute their future positions and so predict where they would appear at a given day and hour. This in itself was no light task, but it was made all the more difficult by the currently accepted theory of planetary motion. A legacy of Greek science, it was based on the principle that all the celestial bodies travelled in exactly circular paths—a principle that owed more to aesthetic and philosophical consideration than to observation. For although it seemed evident enough to anyone with even a superficial knowledge of science that the stars moved in a circle since they were fixed to the inside of a globe, and that the Sun and Moon moved in circles too, circular motion for the planets was not a logical interpretation of astronomical observation. The planets do not pursue a straightforward course across the sky: every so often they appear to stand still, then retrace their steps, stand still once again, and at last go forward in their original direction. Whatever the explanation of this may be, it obviously cannot be accounted for by simple circular motion. But the Greek philosophers were not prepared to accept the implications of what they saw. They were seeking an all-embracing scheme of nature —divine, human and material—and if observation in a particular instance did not fit into this scheme, then they must look behind observation and, if need be, cast aside obvious appearances. And it was into this scheme of the universe that circular motion fitted so well. What could be more appropriate for an eternal celestial body than motion in a circle, since a circle has neither beginning nor end, and is it not the most elegant of shapes both visually and mathematically? If, then, a celestial body is changeless, a planet's motion must be uniform and it must not hurry over one section of its orbit or dawdle along another. To the aesthetic mind this elegant economy weighed heavily in favour of regular circular planetary motion, and tied in perfectly with the conception of a spherical universe to confine the stars, and a spherical Earth fixed firmly at the centre of creation. This beautifully basically simple scheme had ousted the hypothesis of a flat Earth from Greek science as early as the first half of the fourth century B.C., but aesthetically satisfying though it might be, for the next 1,800 years it was to prove a millstone around the neck of astronomers.

In essence it was only necessary to 'save the phenomena'—to account for the observations—by mixing together uniform motions in the appropriate way, but this was easier said than done. To the Greeks, who possessed a flair for geometry, this intellectual challenge was in itself enough, and over the years they provided a number of possible ways out. Each was an improvement over those that had gone before, but it was not until the middle of the second century A.D. that the problem appeared to have found its final solution. Then, in the Museum at Alexandria, which over the centuries could boast of scholars like Euclid (*fl.* 3rd. cent. B.C.) and Archimedes (*c.* 287–212 B.C.), the astronomer Claudius of Ptolemais (*c.* 150 A.D.) produced his answer—a carefully computed system that made use of a

15

geometrical device of great elegance invented some three and a half centuries earlier by Apollonius of Perge.

Claudius was an amazing man. Usually known as Ptolemy from his town of birth, and not from any connection with the Ptolemaic kings with whom he was persistently confused by medieval and Renaissance illustrators, he displayed his genius over a wide field. He made original studies in optics, was a brilliant mathematician and his contributions to geography and astronomy were such as to exert a profound influence for more than fourteen centuries. But it is with his compendious treatise on astronomy that we are concerned, a treatise which has come down to the western world with the debased Arabic title of *Almagest* (The Greatest). Yet whatever we may call it—and its original Greek title *The Mathematical Collection* is now known—it is a monumental work that puts planetary astronomy on a firm foundation: provided, of course, one accepts the conceptions of a fixed Earth and uniform circular motion. The manner in which Ptolemy extricated himself from the impasse of observed planetary motions and squared these with the aesthetic demands that he never questioned, was to develop Apollonius's idea of the epicycle and deferent. This ingenious system accounted for the observed planetary movements by imagining that every planet moved with a double circular motion—the planet itself orbiting in a circle (the epicycle) about a point which itself orbited in a larger circle (the deferent) about the Earth. At least, that was the essence of it, but Ptolemy developed the idea much further and with a great deal of precision. While he placed the large circles, the deferents, with their centres at the centre of the Earth, he did away with uniform motion around them, replacing this instead by uniform motion about quite different points, each some distance from the Earth's centre. Again, he used not one but a whole number of little epicycles which rocked as they rotated round the deferent. It was a nightmare of complexity, but it worked well and, what is more, it could be modified when observation rendered modification necessary. Small wonder, then, that it did duty for so long and was even being argued about in the seventeenth century—although then it was not astronomers but theologians who supported it for, unhappily, it had become embroiled in a vast synthesis of Christian orthodoxy and natural knowledge.

16

The idea that the Earth was permanently fixed in the centre of the universe was not everywhere accepted in Greek times. There were those who believed otherwise. Philolaos of Croton (c. 450 B.C.), a follower of the religious leader and mathematician Pythagoras (c. 550 B.C.), thought that the Earth orbited in space, not round the Sun but round a mythical central fire, and opposite to it orbited an antichton or counter-Earth. Philolaos's suggestion was put forward for mystical reasons, since he wanted the total number of planetary bodies, including the Sun and Moon, to be ten, but a more scientific spirit motivated later protagonists of a moving Earth. Hiketas (5th cent. B.C.), another Pythagorean, Herakleides of Pontos (4th cent. B.C.), and a few others, suggested that the Earth rotated once a day about its axis, so accounting for the rising and setting of the Sun, Moon and stars. But it is to Aristarchos of Samos (c. 310–230 B.C.) that we must turn to find a fully-fledged heliocentric theory, putting the Sun at the centre of the universe in place of the Earth. Aristarchos proposed his ideas in the second two decades of the second century B.C., and it is clear that he was an astronomer and mathematician of considerable ability. He it was who first computed the relative distances of the Sun and Moon, using observations based on an ingenious geometrical scheme of his own devising. That his results were seriously in error due to the impracticability of his observing methods need not worry us here—the idea and the calculations alone at least show his stature as a theoriest.

Yet simple and effective though his heliocentric hypothesis was—it contained both the earlier idea of the rotation of the Earth on its axis as well as the concept of an orbit about the Sun—it was not pursued. There seem to have been two reasons for this: one, that the general climate of thought was unfavourable to so great a break with tradition, and second, and of far more importance, the idea appeared to be philosophically unsound. Some eighty years before Aristarchos had proposed his heliocentric theory, Aristotle (384–322 B.C.) had already considered the earlier ideas about a moving Earth and had demolished the suggestions of Philolaos in particular by a host of carefully reasoned arguments. The new ideas of Aristarchos did not seem to invalidate Aristotle's conclusions, which, although

17

they have long since been thrown overboard, were a brilliant analysis of the physical world, and even in Ptolemy's time five centuries later remained unchallenged. So for what appeared to be very sound reasons Ptolemy accepted a stationary Earth in the centre of the universe, even though he did admit that a rotation of the Earth about its axis (quite apart from its motion in space) would have simplified his task enormously. However, so strongly do scientific theories tend to grip their adherents that we should not criticise Ptolemy too harshly for his conservatism.

Ptolemy's geocentric theory and Aristotle's physical synthesis form the astronomical heritage that was handed down to posterity. As we have seen, they came to Britain, as to the rest of western Christendom, by way of Islam, first of all in Latin translations prepared from Arabic translations of what were probably only copies of the original Greek text. At all events, one would not expect these versions to have transmitted the old teachings in all their purity, and in fact they included all manner of excrescences in the way of additional ideas or mis-intepretations of the originals. The Ptolemaic and Aristotelian universe was encumbered with the concept of crystal spheres—the idea that, in spite of the device of the deferent and epicycle, all planets including the Sun and Moon were fixed to the inside of spheres (conveniently made of pure transparent crystal, which explained why they could not be observed). This, then, was the theoretical picture of the universe that came to Britain in the thirteenth century, and the one which was accepted by the universities and by the learned community as a whole. There was, it is true, a certain amount of dissatisfaction with some aspects of the physics of Aristotle's universe. Roger Bacon (c. 1214–1292) at Oxford attacked the Aristotelian explanation of the flight of a projectile, since he quite rightly felt that the belief that it moved only because the air pushed it was too hard to swallow. Liaison with other Franciscans at the University of Paris showed a similar dissatisfaction there, and led to a doctrine of impetus which transferred the drive from the air to the projectile itself. But so far as astronomy was concerned, this break with Aristotle had no repercussions. The learned world was too imbued with the belief that celestial motions were, quite literally, out of this world and governed by considerations that were essentially different from any which applied to mundane

18

terrestrial phenomena. The heavens were truly a law unto themselves.

This separation lent some credence to astrology, which, although it was spasmodically attacked, continued to flourish. For if the movements of the stars and planets were governed according to the dictates of heavenly beings—and this was the general view—then the belief that they exerted some influence on man the acme of divine creation, was but one step away, and a short step at that. It was a view, too, that permeated the medical treatment of the day. The signs of the zodiac were supposed to have a direct influence on the organs of the body—Leo the Lion had responsibility for the heart, for example—while the planets helped to govern the various humours (liquids) which were to be found in perfect balance only in the healthy individual. And since it was the belief of a number of scholars that the planets were moved by divine beings, and the accepted view of all men that the sphere of the stars was moved either by God himself, or his spirit, the connection between the universe and man, whose spirit was imprisoned during life at the centre of the universe, seemed only natural. Indeed the link between man, the microcosm, and the universe, the macrocosm, was so obvious a truth that it permeated all thinking. The divine concern with human affairs was seen in every possible circumstance, and the heavens were regarded as one of the approved channels for warning of divine displeasure. Comets, which appeared suddenly in the sky displaying their bright heads and long glowing tails, and might remain for days, weeks, or even months, were harbingers of disaster and struck terror into all but the most foolhardy. Certain conjunctions of the planets were considered to be portents of divine chastisement to come, while the glow of the northern lights—the aurora—was variously described as celestial fires or the clash of celestial armies. The interpretation of such celestial phenomena was not always quite so daunting, for a shooting star was one more soul released from purgatory; but, in general, the whole sky was looked upon as a divine message board, to be neglected at one's peril.

Yet during the nascent period between the rediscovery of Greek science and the evolution of the modern scientific outlook, astrology did not blind men to the fact that there were practical problems to be solved. The gradual increase in the length of sea voyages led to a need for accurate star positions in order that the navigator might obtain some idea of his location from simple observations taken on board. As Chaucer says of the sea-captain who joined the Canterbury Pilgrims:

'He knew wel alle the heavens, as they were,
From Gootland to the Cape of Finistere.'

But Chaucer, the author of the best English account of the astrolabe—that elegant instrument for observing the altitudes of stars —also knew that navigation was not merely a matter of being able to recognise the heavens. A navigator required some rudimentary knowledge of the movements of the Moon, if not of the planets as well, and this meant calculations based on planetary theory. These no mariner could undertake: instead he would use the tables that were avilable and which gave him sufficient information to be reasonably accurate. The tables themselves were quite extensive, for they were also used by astrologers and by those who were struggling with the ever present problem of compensating the civil and religious calendars.

The difficulties with the calendars arose because the Christian church, like the Mohammedan, based its calendar on the phases of the Moon. In the days of the nomadic Hebrews this was satisfactory enough, but it was anathema to the settled agricultural civilisation in western Europe. Here a seasonal calendar based on the movement of the Sun was what was needed, and to relate the two gave rise to a most intractable situation. Without becoming involved in the mathematics of the problem, one easily realises the main difficulty on considering that a solar year embracing the four seasons covers approximately $365\frac{1}{4}$ days, whereas the time from new Moon to new Moon is roughly speaking $29\frac{1}{2}$ days; and try as one may, it is impossible to divide one into the other without being left with an awkward fraction. Hence Easter, determined as the first Sunday after the full Moon that appears on or after the 21st March (vernal equinox), provides a thorny problem for the astronomer which becomes abominably complicated if, as was the case in Britain until 1752, the civil calendar itself gets out of step with the seasons. This imbalance was the result of the fact that the solar year is some $11\frac{3}{4}$ minutes short of $365\frac{1}{4}$ days, and while the odd $\frac{1}{4}$ days are taken account of by leap years, the seemingly trifling $11\frac{3}{4}$ minutes grows through the centuries into a significant error. To correct this requires a detailed and accurate knowledge of the Sun's motion across the heavens, and a planetary theory sufficiently sophisticated to allow the Sun's future positions to be calculated with great precision.

For many reasons, then, tables of planetary positions were prepared, based on careful observations, and with future positions computed on the basis of Ptolemy's geocentric theory. First drawn up in the Muslim world at the beginning of the eleventh century and, later, in thirteenth-century western Christendom, they were as accurate as current theory and observational techniques would allow. But their computation was most involved, and it is clear that one compiler at least had doubts about the suitability of the Ptolemaic system. This was Alphonso X of Castille (1226–1284) who, before he ascended the throne, led a team of Christian and Jewish astronomers at Toledo and prepared what became known as the *Alphonsine Tables*. Alphonso said—or is supposed to have said—that if God had consulted him before making the universe, then he would have been able to give him some good advice! True or not, the comment obviously arose from disenchantment with Ptolemy's theory. In the millenium since *Almagest* was written, observational techniques had improved: the telescope had not been invented, but even so the comparatively simple techniques then used had been refined and observations of planetary positions were possible to a far higher degree of accuracy. Herein lay the problem. Every time an observed planetary position was compared with a calculated position, the latter was found to be wrong, and it gradually became clear that the geocentric theory of *Almagest* was in need of improvement. Unhappily no one seems to have thoroughly thought the matter through again— perhaps the authority of Aristotle and Ptolemy was too strong— and improvment merely took the form of adding corrections by piling one epicycle on another. In the end some eighty deferents and epicycles were needed to account for planetary motions, and the labour of computation became unmanageably complex: yet it was not until the mid-sixteenth century that salvation arrived from Poland in the form of Nicholas Copernicus's revolutionary hypothesis.

Copernicus was born in Toruń in northern Poland in February 1473 and was brought up by his uncle who, elected as Bishop of Ermland in 1489, became responsible for the temporal and spiritual well-being of his see. After a wide education at Toruń and Cracow universities where he showed a liking for astronomy and mathematics, and later at Bologna where he read canon law and at Padua where he attended the famous medical school, Copernicus entered his uncle's service and was elected to a canonry at Frauenberg Cathedral. For the most part he devoted himself to his administrative duties and to acting as unpaid physician to the poor. But his interest in astronomy remained. Indeed, it had been stimulated at almost every turn throughout his extensive education; in both Toruń and Cracow he had busied himself with it, egged on a little perhaps by the even greater needs of navigators which became common knowledge at Cracow after Columbus voyaged across the Atlantic. At Bologna he probably lodged with the astronomy professor, a strong critic of Aristotle, and at Padua his study of medicine, far from diverting his attention, would have brought him into contact with astronomy yet again; so it is little wonder that when he could find any free time from his official duties or his medical commitments, he amused himself by making astronomical observations.

Copernicus was not a good observer—the poor accuracy of his measurements of planetary positions proves that—but even his fumbling efforts made it clear to him that theory and observation were poles apart. Predicted and observed positions were in wild disagreement. To a man with Copernicus's educational background, there seemed only one answer: to return to the Greeks, still considered as the fountain-head of all scientific knowledge, and discover for himself what they had really said. The result was electrifying. He found that opinion had not been unanimous and that, as we have seen, there had been suggestions that it was the Sun and not the Earth that was the focal point of the universe. What, he wondered, would be the mathematical consequences of this? Would it prove possible to simplify computation by using a heliocentric system? And, even more to the point, would such a hypothesis make it possible to obtain predicted positions that had some real pretension to accuracy? Copernicus decided to investigate the possibilities in depth, and so set out on a long and tedious voyage of discovery that took

22

more than thirty years to complete. Except for a brief note about his views circulated in 1540, his ideas were only published as *De Revolutionibus Orbium Coelestium* (On the Revolution of the Celestial Spheres), the first copy of which reached him as he was dying in 1543.

In this classic book Copernicus emphatically suggests that the Sun is the centre of the universe, and goes into some detail over the advantages this theory would give. He uses his new idea to explain the march of the seasons and to provide a detailed analysis of planetary motion. He had achieved the apparently impossible: in so doing he refuted Aristotle's arguments against a moving Earth, providing a system of deferents and epicycles that gave a uniform motion centred on the Sun as the hub of the universe, and avoiding the displacements that Ptolemy had had to adopt. In brief, Copernicus had produced a novel system which, whether physically true or not, definitely made the computation of planetary positions less formidable, and naturally appealed to mathematicians.

But no revolutionary idea, no book that presents a new view which breaks abruptly with tradition, can be expected to arrive without arousing animosity. Copernicus clearly appreciated this and he delayed publication as long as he could: indeed, there is good evidence for believing that his heliocentric theory was virtually complete twenty years before he published it and that all he achieved in the interim were minor refinements and corrections. When the book did appear the expected storm broke. First it was attacked by the Protestants, and later by Copernicus's own Roman Catholic church, in spite of a preface explaining that the theory was no more than a mathematical device for simpler calculation and should not be taken as a description of physical reality. This was not Copernicus's preface—it was the work of an editor whom he never met—and there is reason to suppose that he knew nothing of the reference to the crystal spheres that was inserted in the title. But even as a mathematical hypothesis, the theologians considered it too dangerous to leave unchallenged.

Here was a theory that turned away from tradition, a theory that violated the basic assumption that Greek science held an authority in scientific matters similar to the authority of Holy Writ in the religious field. Orthodoxy in religion and in science had been inextricably intertwined when in the thirteenth century

Thomas Aquinas produced his masterly synthesis of Greek science and Christian dogma: divine Aristotle had assumed the stature of St Paul, and to question the teachings of the former was to throw doubts on the doctrines of the latter.

Although Copernicus used the deferents and epicycles of Ptolemy and himself accepted the entire scheme of Aristotelian physics, the theory really demanded a thorough overhaul of all ideas of motion and of the universe. Aristotle had argued that bodies fell to the ground because their natural place was the centre of the universe, yet if the Earth were a mere planet in orbit, then why should they not fall to the centre of the Sun? And if the Earth moved round the Sun, why should the Moon follow it? Why should it not be left behind, moving in its own orbit round the Sun? To explain these anomalies required a completely new physics and, moreover, there was no observational proof to support Copernicus. If the movement of the Earth was a physical fact rather than a mathematical fiction, then at different seasons of the year we should be closer to different parts of the starry sphere. The stars in the sign of Virgo ought to look closer in March than at any other time in the year, and in May it ought to be those in Scorpio. Yet no change could be detected, even with the most refined instruments of the day. If the new heliocentric theory were true, then the sphere of the stars had to be assumed to be of enormous size—a claim that Copernicus did in fact make. But a universe with a vast gap between the sphere of the most distant planet, Saturn, and the sphere of the stars was, in the minds of most philosophers, an affront to God. Surely He would not have designed a universe with an immense empty space that served no purpose?

And so it was that the late sixteenth-century astronomer faced a new challenge. He had a useful tool that made his computations easier and, moreover, a tool that possessed greater mathematical elegance than any before it. But it was a tool with the most dire consequences. The whole structure of the physical universe might be laid low with it, and the divine relationship of the universe radically altered. Was this too high a price to pay? Luther (1483–1546) claimed it was: Copernicus, he said, was a fool who would upset the whole science of astronomy, and even the gentler Melancthon (1497–1560) attacked the theory with a host of arguments both scriptural and physical. But the

Protestant theologians were at this time wedded to a literal interpretation of the Bible and their attitude was as understandable as it was misguided. Only the philosopher with a scientific turn of mind could really assess the situation, but even for him the answer was not easy to find. A hard battle had to be fought if the scientific habits of a millenium were to be cast aside. In Renaissance Italy this had to wait for Galileo, but in Elizabethan England the change came earlier, and was greeted with a tolerance not found elsewhere.

II

The New World
of the Renaissance

ELIZABETH I came to the throne on 17 November 1558, eleven years after the death of Copernicus and the publication of his *De Revolutionibus*. She took command of an economically debilitated country, wracked by four years of religious persecution under Mary I, but a country with a love of learning that nevertheless still flourished. There was a popular interest in astronomy among the nobility, the merchants and most educated men, as the flow of publications evinces. The *Sphaera Mundi* of Sacrobosco, written in the thirteenth century, ran into edition after edition, and the simpler fourth-century *Sphaera* of Proclus had a still wider currency after the publication of William Salysburye's English translation in 1550. But the situation is best shown by the fact that between 1481 and Elizabeth's accession, a total of thirty-one books on astronomy saw the light of day.

The year 1481 is significant, because it was then that William Caxton printed and published his first scientific book *The Mirrour of the World*, his own translation of a thirteenth-century French poem describing the physical universe, and this was followed by many others, most of them translations of earlier works. All these books dealt with the old astronomy, but though they expounded the Aristotelian universe and the Ptolemaic system, they indicate a demand that could only be created by a lively interest in the subject and point to an informed opinion aware of the difficulties that Copernicus set out to overcome.

Perhaps the most important contributor to the sound teaching that preceded the astronomical revolution was Robert Recorde (*c.* 1510–1558), who studied at both Oxford and Cambridge and was court physician to Edward VI and Mary I. As well as being a good classical scholar and a mathematician, credited with the invention of the equals sign (=), Recorde had a flair for clear and simple English which he employed in a number of mathematical textbooks that remained standard works for decades. These he planned as a series, possibly based on the lectures he gave at Oxford, and the first, *Grounde of Artes,* appeared in 1543, the same year as *De Revolutionibus.* Next came the first book on geometry to be published in English, and finally, in 1556, his astronomical textbook *The Castle of Knowledge.* This is an extensive survey of astronomical knowledge written in the popular form of a dialogue between teacher and pupil, and it is extremely thorough in all but one aspect—it fails to discuss fully the various theories of planetary motion. Although Recorde describes the basic difference between the Copernican and Ptolemaic theories he does not go into enough detail to commit himself directly. He goes no further than making his pupil call the Copernican system a 'vaine phantasie', to which the teacher retorts severely 'You are too yonge to be a good judge in so great a matter: it passeth farre your learninge, and theirs also that are much better learned then you, to improve his [Copernicus's] supposition by good argumentes, and therefore you were best to condemne no thing that you do not well understand.' Perhaps Recorde wanted more time to mull over the novel Copernican hypothesis, but his remark makes it seem likely that had his promised sequel been written it would have supported the theory which he, for one, clearly did not take to be a mathematical fiction.

In the event, the first open advocacy of Copernican astronomy came from that incredible figure, John Dee (1527–1608), magical alchemist and erudite mathematician. Dee was born in London but it was while up at Cambridge that he developed an interest in magic—not the superstitious magic of the charlatan, but mystical Hermetism. Unfortunately this was to bring him into disrepute, since what he thought was not understood by others and his desire for true knowledge never completely appreciated. The Hermetic tradition that he followed was a complex of mysteries based, so its practitioners believed, on the teachings of Hermes Trismegistus, who was supposed to have been an Egyptian sage contemporary with Moses. With seemingly prophetic allusions to Christianity and a good deal of the occult, Hermes's works were a power in the Renaissance, which so revered the learning of the past, and they coloured the outlook of many learned men whose aim was to form a synthesis of the entire universe. This grandiose hope was not to be a mere physical synthesis such as Ptolemy had achieved, but one that embraced all creation from the stars to the natural elements with their magical influences, from man as a physical and spiritual being to the entire hierarchy of the spirit world of angels, archangels and the diety himself. The teaching was wrapped in mystery, allusions were tortuous to confound the uninitiated, and often they were only understood—if understood at all—by whichever Hermetist uttered them. Yet for all the fantastic incomprehensibility that surrounded Hermetism, in spite of the mystical interpretations of perfectly normal phenomena, and even in spite of the fact, unknown at the time, that Hermes Trismegistus was an anachronism, a golden thread of honesty did exist. There was a true desire to find the philosopher's stone that would provide an answer to all things and usher in a better world. At least this was so in the case of the sincere practitioners of whom Dee was undoubtedly one: were he not, he would never have thrown over the teaching of so ancient a philosopher as Ptolemy in favour of the new ideas of Copernicus.

In 1556, the astronomer John Feild produced his own almanac for 1557. Written in Latin, it openly avowed in its title that the astronomical tables it contained were prepared for the latitude of London and were based on the Copernican theory. This was a departure indeed, and since the whole volume was prepared for a learned readership, it needed a learned preface explaining the Copernican system and the advantages it offered. Since Feild had been persuaded to prepare his almanac by Dee, it was to Dee that he handed the task of preparing such explanation as the tables required. The burden of Dee's preface is brief and to the point. Current tables of planetary positions were seriously in error and new ones were needed: since newer tables were available (although not computed specifically for British use) these should be used with the planetary theory of Copernicus as the method for computing future positions. Dee thus clearly recognized the superior accuracy obtainable with the heliocentric theory, but whether he accepted its physical reality is not made clear in the preface.

The Dee preface was significant, not merely because it was the first open advocacy of the heliocentric theory in Britain, but also because it exerted considerable influence. Dee's reputation was immense. He was a friend of all the most important scientific men of the day and corresponded with the leading scientists on the Continent; in addition he acted as technical adviser to navigators, especially Martin Frobisher, Walter Raleigh and, it seems almost certain, Francis Drake as well. At his house in Mortlake he gave advice to emissaries from Elizabeth I (to whom he was later to act as astrologer) and numbered among his pupils Philip Sidney and his family. Dee's laboratory and private library at Mortlake containing original scientific manuscripts, including some by Roger Bacon, formed a vitally important centre of learning at a time when the standard of scholarship at Oxford and Cambridge was in a period of decline. Yet in spite of his great erudition, he was basically a simple man and credited other scholars with his own integrity of approach, and it was in this way that he became the dupe of the charlatan Edward Kelly (*fl.* 1575), who was well enough versed in the vocabulary of Hermetism to be able to exploit Dee's learning and reputation. His association with Kelly saddened the end of Dee's life, for his name was blackened and public opinion turned against him. For posterity, the tragedy of Dee's fall from grace was the sacking of his laboratory and library by a superstitious mob, and the burning of his books and manuscripts, including those by Bacon, which he had hoped would form the nucleus of a national collection.

Dee was that strange phenomenon, the embryonic scientist of the new learning with feet firmly fixed in the mire of medieval magic. If like another wilder and less scholarly Hermetist, Giordano Bruno, he had been martyred at the stake, perhaps he would be more thought of today and the significant impetus he gave to the Copernican theory applauded more generously. That Dee's preface had its due effect becomes clear from subsequent events, but this was not his only powerful essay into the astronomical world. In November 1572 a 'new star' appeared in the constellation of Cassiopeia, a rare event that excited both astronomers and astrologers. We now know that this was a supernova—a star that suddenly explodes, ejecting most of its substance as a sphere of hot and intensely bright gas—but in the sixteenth century no full explanation was available. To the orthodox philosopher it was some phenomenon in the upper air rather than in the heavens, since Aristotelian physics confined all change to beneath the sphere of the Moon: the heavens themselves were immutable. At its brightest, the supernova out-shone Venus, the 'evening star', but seventeen months later it had faded until it was scarcely visible. What had happened? Why had it faded? Dee pondered the matter and came forward with the opinion not only that the object was a real star, but also that its fading glory was caused by the star moving away in a straight line from the Earth. This view, which he published in 1573 in a book on the trigonometrical problem of discovering stellar distances, hit squarely at the accepted Aristotelian doctrine that the universe was a plenum of crystal spheres, since a star travelling as he proposed would have to pass through them.

Further evidence of the interest in the new approach to astronomy came from Dee's brilliant pupil Thomas Digges, who was born in about 1546. Digges's father, Leonard (?–c. 1571), was also an eminent scientist and produced a well-known popular perpetual almanac, a *Prognostication Everlasting,* but when his son was only thirteen it was Dee who took upon himself the task of educating the boy. According to Thomas's own testimony, Dee was a 'second parent' and, for his part, Dee thought highly of his pupil: 'a most worthy heir in mathematics'. Using an extremely accurate large cross-staff that Dee and the navigator Richard Chancellor (?–1556) had built, Digges also observed the supernova and his results were published at the end of February 1573 in the front of his own book on stellar distances, *Alae seu Scalae Mathematicae.* They were taken up in Denmark by Tycho Brahe (1546–1601), whose famous observatory on the little island of Hven, opposite Elsinore, was an institution of considerable size for that time. Brahe, the greatest observer of his age, is the man always associated with observations of this supernova, and in 1573 he too published a book discussing his results. Yet thirty-five years later he paid tribute to Digges, devoting more pages of his *Astronomiae Instauratae Progymnasmata* (Exercises in the Restoration of Astronomy) to Digges's observations than to those of any other astronomer. Both Digges and Brahe had come to the same conclusions: the new star was indeed a star and certainly not a meteorological phenomenon. Their angular measurements showed that the 'parallax' of the star was less than that of the Moon—in other words the Moon was closer to us than was the new star. Dee said the same; as William Camden wrote in his *Annales*,[1] 'Thomas Digges, and John Dee, Gentlemen, and Mathematicians amongst us, have learnedly proved by paralactic doctrine, that it was in the celestial, not in the elementary region.'

Thomas Digges had established his reputation in 1571 when he completed and published his father's book *A Geometrical practise, named Pantometria,* which became the best available vernacular text on the practical use of geometry for surveying and measurement. The *Alae* greatly enhanced this reputation and in the long term was the more important of the two books, for it advanced the development of astronomy in England. Not only did it contain Digges's assertion that the supernova was a truly celestial phenomenon, but it went on to support the Copernican hypothesis, expressing also his suggestion that the supernova, still visible as he wrote, was 'an especially opportune occasion, for proving whether the motion of the Earth set forth in the Copernican theory, is the sole reason why this star is diminishing in magnitude [brightness]'. Digges postulated that if this were the cause, then the star might be expected to continue fading until the spring (six months after it had appeared so bright) and then to increase again in magnitude—if not to its former brilliance, at least to 'unusual magnitude and splendor'. This was a quite logical proposal in the light of the information available to Digges but, unhappily for the protagonists of heliocentricity, supernovae do not behave in this way, and they had to look further for proof to convince the unconverted.

Digges did not forsake Copernicus because his theory of the supernova was at fault. Doubtless he was encouraged by the fact that his observations had at least achieved one thing, disproof of the existence of the crystal spheres of Aristotelian doctrine, and that here he had the support of Brahe whose work was internationally recognized. If Aristotle were wrong over this, then in what other matters, including the movement of the planets, might it be possible to find a flaw? Digges's next step was therefore to probe deeper into the Copernican system and draw up a description of it in English. This he published as a

31

The pre-Copernican universe, with the Earth at the centre and outside it the spheres of the planets and of the 'fixed' stars. The four 'elements' of Aristotelian physics—earth, air, fire and water—are shown at the centre, the sphere of water surrounding the Earth, air (with clouds) above that and lastly the sphere of fire. From *Cosmographia* by Peter Apian, edited by Gemma Frisius, Antwerp, 1539.

(*Ronan Picture Library*)

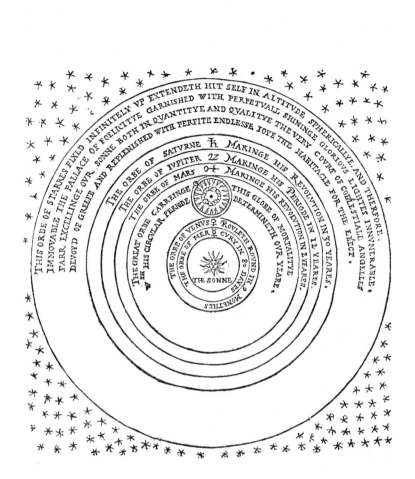

The infinite Copernican universe with the Sun at the centre and the Earth as an orbiting planet, as envisaged by Thomas Digges in the 1576 edition of his father's *Prognostication Everlasting*.

(*Royal Society*)

C

supplement to the 1576 edition of his father's *Prognostication everlasting*, calling it *A Perfit Description of the Caelestiall Orbes according to the most aunciente doctrine of the Pythagoreans, lately revived by Copernicus and by Geometricall Demonstrations approved.* The supplement included a complete translation of the principal parts of the first section of *De Revolutionibus*—the parts that contained the essential facts and arguments of the heliocentric theory—and a diagram of the heliocentric system. In this drawing and in the supplement there appears a startling suggestion—the idea of an infinite universe. Gone completely is the belief in a sphere of stars, the closed spherical ball of a universe conceived by the Greeks and accepted by Copernicus.

The legend that Digges placed on his diagram, round the inside of the circle at which the realm of the stars begins, is breathtaking in its significance: 'This orbe of starres fixed infinitely up extendeth hit self in altitude sphericallye, and therefore immovable the pallace of foelicitye garnished with perpetuall shininge glorious lightes innumerable. Farr excellinge our sonne both in quantitye and qualitye the very court of coelestiall angelles. Devoid of greefe and replenished with perfite endlesse ioye the habitacle for the elect.' The stars are drawn extending to the edges of the diagram and thus, in the mind of the reader, to the uttermost distance of space. The legend is interesting because it mentions not only the infinite nature of space but also the idea that the stars are like the Sun, and far excel it in 'qualitye'. The suggestion that the stars are Suns and are of different sizes was not new: it had been made long before by the Italian Pietro Manzolli (*fl.* 1510–1540) (usually known as Palingenius) in his descriptive poem *Zodiacus vitae,* first published in English in 1560, and from which Digges was fond of quoting. But Palingenius still thought of the stars as fixed on a sphere, and it was Digges who threw the idea aside and appreciated that objects that appeared so bright but lay at vast distances might well exceed the Sun in size.

And so it was that since the supplement appeared in numerous editions of *Prognostication everlasting*, the heliocentric theory in Britain became linked with an infinite distribution of the stars. Such views could not be held in isolation, and an assault on Aristotlelian physics was a necessary part of the new thinking;

34

but in England the attack lacked the bitterness that it engendered on the Continent. Digges was quite specific in his attitude. In writing about the arguments he had quoted against 'the Earthes stability', he goes on to say 'I cannot a little commende the modestie of that grave Philosopher *Aristotle*, who seeing (no doubt) the insufficiency of his owne reasons in seeking to confute the Earthes motion, useth these words *De his explicatum est ea qua potuimus facultate* [These things are explained by the easiest possible method] howbeit his disciples have not with like sobriety maintayned the same.'[2] Whether or not Aristotle would have agreed with Digges's interpretation, the attitude of mind is the important thing, and it was shared by other English scholars. Robert Recorde had been equally balanced in his opinion of Ptolemy. 'No man can worthely praise Ptolemye', he wrote in his *Castle of Knowledge,* 'his travell being so great, his diligence so exact in observations, and conference with all nations, and all ages, and his reasonable examination of all opinions, with demonstrable confirmation of his owne assertion, yet muste you and all men take heed, that both in him and in al mennes workes, you be not abused by their autoritye, but evermore attend to their reasons and examine them well, ever regarding more what is saide, and how it is proved, then who saieth it: for autoritie often times deceaveth many menne.'[3]

This tolerance to the early astronomers was vital if balanced judgements of scientific theories were to be made. It was necessary, too, to do as Recorde suggested, and judge only on the facts, not on the exalted standing of an individual. Digges echoed these sentiments as well as laying particular emphasis on the importance of observation in forming a theoretical opinion. In the section of his *Alae* which deals with the supernova, he criticises the Greeks for forming their theories first, and only later seeking after 'true Parallaxes and distances', explaining that they should rather 'have proceeded in inverse order, and from Parallaxes, which have been observed and are known, they ought to have examined Theories'.[4] Digges even went so far as to advocate internationally co-ordinated planning of astronomical observation, but here he was some four and a half centuries ahead of his day.

Seven years after the publication of the *Perfit Description,*

Giordano Bruno (1548–1600) visited England. Bruno, originally a Dominican friar, had been ostracised by his order, and now he travelled Europe energetically criticising his church and propounding the most extravagant Hermetism. In England he was under the protection of the French ambassador, and through him obtained introductions to a number of scholars. He may not have met Dee, who was out of the country for part of this year, but he probably met Digges on at least one occasion, and it is known that he visited Oxford, where he was looked on as a mountebank. It was at Oxford in 1583 that Bruno extolled the Copernican theory, but whether his praise was based on an appreciation of its scientific merit or a delight at its symbolic attack on authority is debatable. His audience was unimpressed.

However, the main reason for his advocacy would seem to be the way in which *De Revolutionibus* undermined the establishment and his wish to be free of 'pedants' like Aristotle, for in his book *La Cena de le ceneri* (The Ash Wednesday Supper) published in London in 1584, he speaks of Copernicus as someone to whom 'we owe our liberation from several false prejudices of the commonly received philosophy, which I will not go so far as to call blindness. Yet he himself did not much transcend it; for being more a student of mathematics than of nature he was not able to penetrate deeply enough to remove himself and others from the pursuit of empty enquiries and turn their attention to things constant and certain.'5 So far so good—this appears to be firmly in the logical scientific tradition we would expect from Recorde, Digges or Dee—and we might look forward to Bruno expounding further, criticising, perhaps, a heliocentric system that still held to Aristotelian ideas of motion, or to the crystal spheres. He does expound further, but not in the way expected. The Earth moves, he claims, 'that it may renew itself and be born again, for it cannot endure for ever in the same form. For those things which cannot be eternal as individuals ... are eternal as a species; and substances which cannot be everlasting under the same aspect, change themselves into other appearances. For the material substance of all things is incorruptible. ... Therefore, since death and dissolution are unfitted to the whole mass of which this globe, this star, consists, and complete annihilation is impossible to all nature, the Earth changes its parts from time to time and in a certain order and so renews itself.... And I say that the cause of its motion, not only its motion as a whole but of all its parts, is in order that it may pass through vicissitudes....'⁶

This is not science, even sixteenth-century science. It shows a medieval cast of mind, and one full of magical anthropomorphic illusions at that. Yet there are those who wish to find in Bruno a precursor of modern scientific attitudes. Neglecting men like Dee and Digges, they suggest that it was Bruno who, if he did not bring Copernicanism to Britain, at least made it acceptable. They would see in a phrase like 'complete annihilation is impossible to all nature' a presage of the modern doctrine of conservation of matter. Yet Bruno's reception at Oxford and, even more, his writings, make this incredible: it is indeed no more than reading history backwards. His outpourings contrast strangely with those of Dee, Hermetist though he was. Take, for example, the following extracts from Dee's preface to Henry Billingsley's English translation of Euclid, a work which was published in 1570 and exerted a considerable influence on British mathematical learning. After defining the three sources of knowledge—supernatural, mathematical, and material—he points out that 'A mervaylous newtralitie have these thinges *Mathematicall,* and also a strange participation betwene thinges supernaturall, immortall, intellectuall, simple and indivisible: and thynges naturally, mortall, sensible, compounded and divisible.... In Mathematicall reasoninges ... onely a perfect demonstration, of truthes certaine, necessary, and invincible: universally and necessaryly concluded: is allowed as sufficient for an Argument exactly and purely Mathematicall.'⁷ Moreover Dee was a strong supporter of the experimental approach. Later in the same work he says ' ... the Naturall Philosopher disputeth and maketh goodly shew of reason: And the Astronomer, and the Opticall Mechanicien, put some thynges in *Experience*: but neither, all, that they may: nor yet sufficiently, and to the utmost, those, which they do. There, then, the *Archemaster* [experimental scientist] steppeth in, and leadeth forth on, the *Experiences*, by order of his doctrine *Experimentall*, to the chief and finall power of Naturall and Mathematicall Artes.'⁸

These extracts have been given at length because the arrival of the Copernican system in England was the bedrock on which all later developments were founded, and they are important to help correct the distorted picture that is so often accepted. Dee may not have provided a model of concise English prose—this was something no Hermetist was likely to find possible—and his own ventures into experimental science were not always of the happiest, but he did propound sound science. And as he was a mathematician of great ability and reputation his influence was too considerable to neglect. As for Bruno, his writing was part religious polemic, part fertile imagination and above all a plea for the full development of the Hermetic tradition. True, Bruno suggested that other celestial bodies were inhabited and, more significant, that some stars were to be found in pairs rather than alone—a discovery not made observationally until two centuries later—but his suggestions were based on his mystical beliefs, not on scientific reasoning.

Bruno's writings are always remembered and referred to in connection with the Copernican theory, and particularly its rejection by the Roman Catholic Church, because in 1600 he was burned at the stake in Rome. Yet his immolation was not occasioned by his scientific views but by his religious unorthodoxy. He passionately and earnestly believed that it would be best for mankind if there were freedom of speech, of opinion and of religion, and he attacked Christians for their evils, their schisms and for the fact that they had destroyed the true and good religion of mystical ancient Egypt. For a time he hoped for a practical salvation of mankind through the house of Navarre, but on the murder of the liberal and tolerant Henry III, Bruno returned to his own Italy, praising the Pope, Clement VIII, as a friend of philosophers, and obviously feeling hopeful that he would at least be allowed to teach and to promulgate his ideas. After all, there was talk of Henry IV becoming a Roman Catholic, and perhaps Bruno would be allowed to have his way within the church. But he sadly misjudged the situation, as a man with a high opinion of himself and a strong sense of mission is liable to do, and he was imprisoned by the Inquisition. A year later he was executed.

Bruno's death was in no way a martyrdom for science: it was a penalty for unorthodoxy and heresy. Yet it was in his condemnation by the Inquisition that Bruno's support of the Copernican theory had its real effect, for, in Italy at least, the theory became linked with his religious polemics and heresy. The Dominicans in particular had a right to feel bitter, for it was their order that Bruno had rejected, and they were the first Roman Catholics to preach against Copernicanism when Galileo (1564–1642) praised its virtues publicly. But this was in Italy: in Britain Bruno's ideas had no such effect.

Galileo is remembered for many reasons, but in popular legend it is for his forced recantation in 1633 of the Copernican theory, the reality of the motion of the Earth, and his supposed remark, *sotto voce, 'E pur si muove'* (But it does move). However, though this saying is apocryphal, Galileo should indeed be remembered, and for his positive not his negative contributions. His work lay in three main fields: the use of the telescope, support of the Copernican hypothesis, and the foundation of mathematical physics. The latter fits more conveniently into a later chapter, but the telescope more properly belongs here. Galileo was not, and never laid any claim to be, the original inventor of the telescope, but it is generally agreed that he was the first to use it for examining the heavens. The instrument with which he did this he designed himself from reports of Dutch telescopes that came on sale some time late in 1608 or very early the following year. In essence its design was that of the 'Galilean' opera glass still available at some theatres, and it suffers from the defect of being able to show only a minute portion of the sky at any one time. The instrument had other defects, but notwithstanding these Galileo was able to use it and achieve marvels of deduction. He viewed the Moon and saw craters and valleys on its surface. He observed the evening star—the planet Venus—and noted that it presented phases similar to the Moon. The planet Jupiter he found to be attended by four orbiting satellites, and as for the stars themselves he discovered two new and significant facts: first, that many more stars could be observed with a telescope than could ever be seen with the naked eye and, second, that the hazy band of light that had become known as the Milky Way was composed of myriads of separate stars.

These observations were in themselves astounding enough, but in Galileo's hands they became revolutionary. He used the satellites of Jupiter to demolish the anti-Copernican argument that if the Earth moved in fact rather than in fiction, the Moon would be left behind. The phases of Venus he used as another prop to support the heliocentric hypothesis. With the existence of a pitted and irregular lunar surface he was able to demolish the Aristotelian doctrine that celestial and terrestrial bodies were essentially different, and the additional stars he saw proved that there were things to be seen in the universe which not even the most brilliant Greek philosophers could have known. But Galileo's greatest quality was his perseverance and, not content with the observational discoveries he had made, he began to lay the foundations for a new physical synthesis of the universe, to replace by a new set of concepts the now outdated Aristotelian physics that Copernicus had used. By mathematical analysis of simple physical observations on moving bodies and by induction from his telescopic observations, he was able not only to lay down a method of research that has been used ever since, but also to provide some laws of motion on which even Isaac Newton was only too ready to acknowledge his debt.

Some time in May 1609, Galileo heard the rumours that led him to build his first telescope, and then to construct two larger and improved instruments. These he used for the great series of observations that he published in March 1610 under the title *Sidereus Nuncius* (Sidereal Messenger). But British astronomers were not far behind, if behind at all, for in England in July 1609 Thomas Harriott, with friends and pupils, was observing the Moon with a telescope. When *Sidereus Nuncius* appeared, with drawings that were not especially good, he settled down to preparing the first real map of the Moon made with the aid of a telescope. It was a competent map, far more detailed than Galileo's drawings, and it enumerated almost fifty separate features.

Not a great deal is known of Harriott. He was born in Oxford in 1560 and later attended the university: he was in the service of Walter Raleigh, went with him to Virginia in 1584, and the next year published an account of the province and of the great discovery, tobacco. Later his patron was the Earl of Northumberland, and although he afterwards produced works on mathematics, his astronomical observations were mostly made at the beginning of the seventeenth century. He seems to have used a telescope of his own construction, but whether his information came from Holland or whether he obtained the details from British philosophers is unknown. Indeed the early history of the telescope is still a mystery. Three Dutch opticians laid claim to the original invention, but there are obscure passages both in the work of Thomas Digges and his contemporary Giambattista della Porta, and even in the writings of Roger Bacon, that indicate that combinations of mirrors or lenses were known to make distant objects appear closer. Yet it is still not clear how much was known—whether, as Digges seems to suggest in his additions to his father's *Pantometria*, some optical instrument was used for surveying, and if so whether anyone had the imagination to look at the heavens through such a device. Digges died in 1591 after nine years as muster-master general to the British forces in the Low Countries, and his astronomical work seems to have been cut short in 1580. Harriott died in 1621, having never published anything of his astronomical observations in spite of a great deal of persuasion by his friends. But the first through his books, and both through their many personal contacts and great reputations as scholars, had stimulated a new and lively impetus to astronomical research that was to gather enormous momentum.

By the third decade of the seventeenth century, the Copernican theory had settled down in England, allied with the concept of an infinite universe of stars. The telescope had finally banished the Ptolemaic system and all would have been straightforward but for the hybrid planetary system that Tycho Brahe proposed. Brahe's orthodox Protestantism had recoiled from the idea of the movement of the Earth, but his astronomical soul would not allow him to be so conservative as to cling to the Ptolemaic universe, especially after his observations of the supernova. He therefore made proposals which were, in essence, a combination of both systems. The Earth was still to be the centre of the universe, fixed and immobile, thus satisfying the scriptures, with the Moon and the Sun in orbit round it. But the difference lay in the suggestion that the rest of the planets orbited round the Sun. This was purely a compromise, and as Brahe was not a good enough mathematician, he never worked out the full theoretical implications of his theory. Even so the approach seemed to many philosophers a way of escape from the revolution of thought inherent in thoroughgoing Copernicanism, and he was not alone in suggesting it—a few others hit on the same idea. Although now almost forgotten, this hybrid system had a great

41

vogue, and was still being seriously discussed in France as late as the middle of the seventeenth century.

Brahe's planetary compromise was made known to a few savants, including Dee and Digges, in 1558, but it only became widely available when his great pupil Johannes Kepler (1571–1630) saw Brahe's *Progymnasmata* through the press in 1602. It found its way into popular books on astronomy and so became known to the general British reader. But in Britain the heavy hand of Aristotle had already been pushed aside and, moreover, another factor was at work. In 1600 William Gilbert (1540–1603) had published his important *De Magnete*. This was a brilliant foray into the mysterious phenomenon of magnetism, and by a series of experiments and a good measure of careful reasoning, Gilbert was able to suggest that the Earth must be considered as a giant magnet, thus explaining in one fell swoop all the puzzling behaviour of a magnetic needle. But from the point of view of astronomy, the most significant part of the book was the last eight chapters, in which Gilbert demolished all the physical arguments then current against the rotation of the Earth on its axis.[9] With arguments for the hypothesis, arguments against the views which proved it could not happen, and even a chapter in which the idea of diurnal rotation is shown to account for various well-known astronomical phenomena, Gilbert provided evidence from his magnetic experiments that appeared to him to be undoubted proof of the Earth's rotation. In *De Magnete* he showed clearly the freedom, mathematical and physical, that the heliocentric hypothesis brought. With this book already in circulation, Brahe's system stood little chance of acceptance in Britain; and where it was advocated it was modified by supposing the Earth possessed diurnal rotation.

On Brahe's death his assistant Kepler stepped into his position of court mathematician to the Emperor Rudolph II, and took over the vast collection of planetary observations that Brahe had accumulated. It was Brahe's hope that Kepler would use these in such a way as to prove the truth of his compromise theory, and although Kepler favoured the Copernican hypothesis his regard for Brahe was such that he decided to let the observations alone lead him to a conclusion and not to allow himself to be influenced by any preconceived ideas. The task of trying to determine the precise paths of the planets from such detailed and accurate observations as Brahe made kept Kepler busy for many years. His painstaking labours, however, proved neither Copernicus nor Brahe exclusively right. Kepler began by analysing the observations of Mars, but try as he would, he could not obtain an exact match between the figures and a Copernican or a Brahian orbit. In the end, much to his surprise he found that the only kind of orbit that would satisy the data was an ellipse. No longer would the Greek supposition that the planets orbited in perfect circles, or combinations of perfect circles, fit the facts supplied by accurate observations. Whichever hypothesis was accepted, the orbits had to be elliptical.

But Kepler was not yet satisfied: planetary motion about an ellipse was not uniform—the velocity varied from point to point. This did not suit Kepler's aesthetic desire for uniformity of motion and, driven on by his personal demon of harmony, by a conviction that there must be some example of divine symmetry in the heavens; he felt that somehow, somewhere in these elliptical paths, there must be a relationship that brought back uniform motion. Observation proved the Sun to be displaced from the centre of the ellipse: therefore about the Sun, the centre of the universe, God must have designed that uniformity to which Kepler's neo-Platonic soul aspired. Further painstaking work allowed him to add two generalities of planetary behaviour to his first 'law' that orbits must be elliptical, with the Sun at one focus of the ellipse. These were his second and third 'laws': the second connected the sizes of the orbits and the time a planet took to complete a revolution about the Sun, and the third demonstrated a relation between the speed of orbital motion at any point and the distance of the planet from the Sun at that point. Why such relationships existed, Kepler did not know, but he went on to discover a fourth 'law', a relationship between the changing velocity of a planet in its orbit and the notes of the musical scale, a mystical discovery with which the more scientific of his contemporaries seem to have been unimpressed. Their interest was centred on the third law, the only law which Kepler stated in really precise detail.

In Britain Kepler's discoveries and ideas were known to Harriott, with whom he kept up a correspondence, but since they could apply equally to a Copernican or a Brahian universe, they could not decide the issue. Gilbert's strong support of Copernicus had far more effect among his countrymen because it had fired their imagination. Even Francis Godwin, Bishop of Llandaff, in his scientific romance *The Man in the Moon: or a discourse of a Voyage thither by Domingo Gonsales* (written in 1601 but not published until 1638), was moved to describe what the voyager saw by recourse to Gilbert's treatise. Other books followed, not all convinced of Gilbert's correctness about terrestrial motion, and controversies arose, controversies echoed by John Donne, whose poems show an intimate understanding of the issues involved. It is clear, too, that from a scientific point of view it was the Copernican system that Donne preferred.

The new scientific spirit, the freedom for enquiry grew. The old astronomy died, its last protagonist in Britain being the vituperative Scotsman Alexander Ross, whose scientific knowledge was not equal to his zeal. Ross's objections were published first in 1634 and then off and on until 1653, mainly in the form of pamphlets; he attacked not only astronomers but anyone who had the temerity to enliven philosophy with new ideas, William Harvey and Thomas Hobbes being among those who received his contumely. But Ross was an exception. Almost every writer of almanacs, of mathematical and astronomical treatises failed to resuscitate the old astronomy of the Greeks. The only controversy that remained was whether Brahe or Copernicus was correct. Since the infinite starry universe of Digges could be applied to both, no satisfactory decision could really be made until the physics of the problem had been studied; and the full analysis of this lay in the future.

British interest in astronomy was widespread and continued, as controversy continued, throughout the reigns of James I and Charles I and beyond. Yet during the close of the sixteenth and the beginning of the seventeenth century the universities were not the places where further work was stimulated: the encouragement of new thinking came from outside, from a private establishment founded within the city of London in 1596. This was Gresham College, the funds for which were provided by the enlightened Elizabethan merchant Thomas Gresham, builder of the Royal Exchange, sometime financial agent to Elizabeth I, and ambassador to the Netherlands. Gresham died in 1579 and in his will left his house in Bishopsgate Street for use as a college, with revenues from the Royal Exchange for its maintenance. The proposal was ill-received by his old university of Cambridge, but Gresham had decided that his system for the organization of a college was to be preferred to the methods in use at either Oxford or Cambridge. He wanted there to be seven resident professors who among them would cover astronomy, divinity, geometry, law, music, physic, and rhetoric, and it was their duty to give public lectures in both English and Latin. The professors of astronomy and geometry were to include in their teaching such practical subjects as surveying, mensuration, and the use of navigational instruments.

The early professors were distinguished men, and the chairs of astronomy and geometry were the first to be established in the country. The Yorkshireman Henry Briggs (c. 1556–1630) was the original professor of geometry. A friend of John Napier, the Scotsman who invented natural logarithms, Briggs transformed these for general use by introducing logarithms 'to the base of 10'—the kind of logarithm used most widely today for reducing the labours of computation—and prepared a vast set of tables to promote their adoption. The first professor of astronomy was Edmund Gunter (1581–1626), who also prepared mathematical tables for use in astronomical calculation, and devised observing instruments and a chain for surveying. And those who succeeded Briggs and Gunter were no less inventive.

The foundation was able—probably just because it was free of the traditions of the universities—to busy itself with practical problems. The professors advised on shipbuilding, they took a lively interest in the practical problems of navigation and, equally important, by engaging the interest of their friends and acquaintances, they spread their gospel of practical science. Gresham College had become an institution on which Thomas Gresham might well have congratulated himself, but it was soon to act as an even greater stimulant to the scientific movement in Britain.

From about the third decade of the seventeenth century, informal weekly meetings had been held at the college, and because of these a number of bright young men of independent outlook developed a thirst for knowledge and learned the importance of practical experiment. Most of them probably read Francis Bacon's book *Novum Organum* (1621), with its advocacy of experimental science for 'the relief of man's estate', and the 'new philosophy' developed apace. After the beheading of Charles I in 1649 followed eleven years of Puritan rule, but they did little to hamper the movement that had begun at Gresham College: meetings continued, and some of the band moved to Oxford where they proselytized their views. Converts were made, meetings 'were numerous and very considerable' as John Wallis the mathematician later put it,[10] and the attraction was clearly the new experimental techniques and results. At the Restoration the movement advanced still further and finally, on 28 November 1660, a galaxy of learned men including Lord Brouncker, a notable mathematician and Chancellor to the queen, Robert Boyle the chemist, Christopher Wren, originally an astronomer and mathematician, and Laurence Rooke the Gresham professor of astronomy, met at the college and formally constituted themselves into a voluntary assocation 'So they might doe something answerable ... for the promoting of Experimentall Philosophy'.[11] A week later, Robert Moray, another of those present on 28 November and a personal friend of Charles II, reported that 'the King had been acquainted with the designe of this Meeting. And he did well approve of it, and would be ready to give encouragement for it.'[12] Charles II was as good as his word, persuaded a little perhaps in the following May by being shown Jupiter's satellites and the rings round Saturn through a large telescope which was technically, at least, his own property. He granted the members the name Royal Society, and in July 1662 signed a royal charter providing certain privileges: he presented them with a mace in silver-gilt, and when entreated for further privileges, granted a second and more extensive charter. Thus the Royal Society of London for Improving Natural Knowledge, now the world's senior scientific society, came into being. Astronomy, indeed all science, was to benefit from the establishment of a body with at least nominal royal backing, whose expressed purpose it was to prosecute the advance of natural philosophy in all its branches.

III

The Problem of Navigation

AFTER THE ROUTING of the Spanish Armada in 1588, Britain was able to sail the high seas and pursue her trade wheresoever she wished. The freedom of the seas was here, but it was a freedom fraught with danger at almost every turn: once out of sight of land a mariner had but small chance of finding where he was, and even if he were lucky, his exact position would still be a mystery. This was purely a problem of navigation and in theory it could be solved; in practice it was another matter.

To determine position on the Earth's surface means knowing two co-ordinates, the latitude and the longitude. To find the latitude—the distance north or south of the equator—is relatively simple. It consists only of determining the altitude above the horizon of the Sun or a star, the positions of which are already known from nautical tables. The sixteenth- and seventeenth-century navigator had a number of devices he could use for this—the astrolabe, the cross-staff, the quadrant and, after 1595, John Davis's back-staff—and it presented no difficulty. It was the finding of longitude that seemed intractable. To determine longitude it was necessary to know not only the altitude of the Sun or of a star, but also the altitude as it reached the meridian (i.e., when it was due south); and, worse still, the time at which this occurred, time here being that measured at the seaport from which the ship had sailed and not the local time on board. The altitude when a body is due south is not hard to determine, and navigators had techniques for this that were satisfactory enough; the nub of the problem was determining time. Mechanical clocks had been devised in the West some time during the thirteenth century, but they were crude affairs and improvement came only slowly. Even three and a half centuries later they still kept poor time and their errors amounted to something like ten minutes a day, far too much for a timepiece to be used at sea. Ten minutes a day sounds little enough, but it means a misplacement in longitude of $2\frac{1}{2}$ degrees, or more than 100 miles at the latitude of London and a distance of 173 miles at the equator. But this was for one day's sailing only. The error was cumulative and so the magnitude of the problem becomes obvious: a satisfactory timepiece for use at sea must have an error no greater than four seconds per day, giving longitude at the equator correct to within about sixty miles on a six week voyage. No sixteenth- or even seventeenth-century timepiece could make any pretence to such a degree of accuracy. Yet if time could not be accurately measured by some kind of clock, then what other ways were there of finding an answer, remembering always that the men who would be using any method that might be devised were not scholars but seamen with little more than a rudimentary knowledge of mathematics?

With the growth of colonization, and with it trade, the national and personal prizes that were at stake sharpened the awareness of the need for accurate navigation—far more than the privations the sailors were likely to suffer on a hopelessly protracted voyage. The only solution seemed to lie with the astronomer, who might conceivably be able to draw up tables of celestial bodies that would allow a navigator to use the heavens as his clock. But this presented further problems: stars themselves could not provide the accurate timekeeping required, and the planets moved too slowly across the sky to be of assistance. The only possible escape from this impasse appeared, in theory, to lie in observations of the Moon or, once the telescope had been invented, of the satellites of Jupiter; the former because the Moon's apparent motion is sufficiently rapid to provide the accuracy required, and the latter because the transits of the satellites as they crossed the planet's disk or disappeared into its shadow could also provide a time indication of sufficient delicacy. It needs little imagination to see that making observations of Jupiter's satellites was likely to be impossible at sea, for it is seldom smooth enough for an observer to train his instrument on to the planet, let alone sit by and observe the behaviour of

A seventeenth century engraving of what has come to be known as Flamsteed House, and which formed the original single building of the Royal Observatory in Greenwich Park.

(*Ronan Picture Library*)

The Octagon Room in Flamsteed House showing observers at work during Flamsteed's time.

(*Royal Greenwich Observatory*)

John Flamsteed, the first Astronomer Royal; engraving by George Virtue from the *Historia Coelestis Britannica*, London, 1725.

(*Ronan Picture Library and Royal Astronomical Society*)

Edmond Halley, the second Astronomer Royal and close friend of Newton; engraving by William Fry from a portrait by Michael Dahl in the possession of the Royal Society, and painted when Halley was about eighty years of age.

(*Ronan Picture Library*)

the satellites. Some ingenious observing platforms were designed to overcome this, all with the basic idea of swinging the observer and his telescope between supports so that he would remain still even in the roughest seas, but in practice none of these was successful, and the astronomer had to concentrate his attention on the Moon. Here the aim was to observe the exact moment when the limb of the Moon's disk approached a particular star, and on a clear night this should not be difficult to observe.

One method of longitude determination using lunar observations was proposed in about 1675 by a Frenchman, Le Sieur de Saint-Pierre, who had obtained an introduction to Louise Quérouaille, Duchess of Portsmouth and one of Charles II's mistresses. Saint-Pierre naturally hoped for some financial reward and begged the duchess to bring him and his scheme to the king's notice, and she was able to help him this far. But he was eventually to be disappointed, for the committee of experts that the king set up to examine Saint-Pierre's claim in due course reported that, while the scheme was good in principle, in practice it was quite useless because the orbit of the Moon was not accurately enough known. The Moon's orbit is extremely complex and subject to a host of disturbances, most particularly from the Sun and from the Earth. Over the months the errors accumulate, and in the seventeenth century lunar theory was totally inadequate for computing the Moon's future position by taking these disturbances into account. So Saint-Pierre received no reward, but perhaps he really did not deserve one, as he was simply passing off as his own suggestions made by another Frenchman some forty years before.

When the committee reported on the unsuitability of the scheme, they explained that what was required was a series of accurate observations of the Moon and of the fixed stars made at every conceivable opportunity and continued over at least one complete lunar cycle of nineteen years. The king accepted the necessity for this and realized that to put the scheme into practice meant employing someone who would devote himself to this specific task. He then commanded that the committee member responsible for the unfavourable report on Saint-Pierre's method should 'apply himself' to the work, and thus it was that John Flamsteed (1646–1719), then twenty-nine, was appointed the first Astronomer Royal. An observatory was required for him to work in and Charles II decided to have one established on a hill in his park at Greenwich, the building to be designed by his 'well-beloved and trusty' Christopher Wren.

Flamsteed already had some practical experience of observing —indeed he would never have been able to make his criticisms of Saint-Pierre's proposals otherwise—and he was typical of the new empirical tradition which thought primarily of accuracy, and appreciated the increased precision that the telescope could provide. Two outstanding young men, both dead by this time, had laid the foundations on which Flamsteed was to build. One, Jeremiah Horrox (1619–1641), was a Cambridge graduate who became curate of a country parish and died at the age of twenty-two; the other, William Gasgoigne (1612?–1644), corresponded with Horrox and was killed at the battle of Marston Moor. Gasgoigne fixed telescopes to his measuring instruments, greatly increasing their accuracy, and it was he who invented the micrometer—a measuring device that could be fixed to the eyepiece of a telescope and would permit precise measurement of such phenomena as the movements of the Jovian satellites and the distance of the Moon's limb from a given star.

Horrox was more of a mathematician than an observer, although he took great care at his telescope and like Gasgoigne was intensely interested in accurate results. Horrox's reputation really rests on two achievements, both of which arose from the errors and inconsistencies he found in even the best planetary tables of the day. The first was his theory of the Moon's motion, an ingenious application of Kepler's elliptical orbits in which he significantly suggested that some of the irregularities which bedevilled the lunar orbit were due to the Sun's influence: this almost half a century before the theory of universal gravitation. The second subject in which Horrox shone was also to do with orbital motion, this time of the planet Venus. Here he noticed a discrepancy between the tables that Kepler himself had worked out and those of Philips von Lansberg, concluded that Venus would cross the disk of the Sun on a particular date in November 1639, and observed the phenomenon. In his short life, Horrox himself made calculations of the Sun's distance, a parameter of special significance in astronomy, and discovered, too, irregularities in the motions of the planets Jupiter and Saturn. Unfortunately Horrox's work was unknown except to his close friends, and later to Flamsteed, and of course it exerted little influence abroad. The early death of this 'excellent Astronomer' as Newton called him,[1] was a tragedy for British astronomy; as the Scots mathematician James Gregory later said after reading his posthumous works, 'I have perused him & am satisfied with him beyond measure; it was a great loss that he dyed so young; many naughtie fellows live to 80.'[2]

As soon as he was appointed 'astronomical observator', Flamsteed set about making accurate observations, but it was not easy for him as so little money was available. In the Royal Warrant for building the observatory it was specifically stated that it should not cost more than £500, and even this sum was to be raised by selling old and decayed gunpowder to merchants who could re-treat it and make it usable for those tasks which did not demand a high degree of dependability. A gate-house demolished at the Tower provided wood, and an old fort at Tilbury bricks, iron and lead; but at least Wren built a fine house 'for the Observator's habitation and a little for pompe', with a beautiful octagonal room from which observations could be made. But those who drew up the Warrant either forgot or ignored the vital question of observing instruments. No provision was made for them and Flamsteed, whose salary was only £100 per annum, could hardly be expected to afford them. Sir Jonas Moore, his patron, and the Royal Society came to his rescue, but when Moore died in 1679, a little over three years after Flamsteed had taken office, there was a threat by his heirs to remove the instruments. Flamsteed had to give way, and only retained with difficulty the ones he had been given. There was nothing for it but to build his own, and in 1683 he constructed a large quadrant. The next year a living at Burstow increased his income a little, and this he considerably supplemented by taking private pupils in astronomy and mathematics. These numbered 140 in the thirty-one years from 1676 to 1709, and their coaching must have hindered the real duties of the Astronomer Royal, especially one like Flamsteed who suffered from ill-health, and who from the start had to work alone without any permanent assistance except a 'silly surly labourer'. Only on his father's death was he at last able to afford the expert assistance of Abraham Sharp, an instrument maker and indefatigable computer whom he had been employing on a casual basis. Sharp built a large mural instrument, with a metal arc and framework nearly seven feet high, and fitted with a telescope. It took him fourteen months to make and cost Flamsteed over £120, but it speeded up the observing work on stellar altitudes and by 1703, Flamsteed had amasssed a collection of more than 30,000 observations, most of which were far more accurate than any previously made.

Having supplied his own instruments Flamsteed took the attitude that the observations he made were his own property, to be published only when they were complete and had been duly corrected for observing errors and faults in the instruments, and reduced to a standard form. What is more, he was determined that all his observations must be published together: only in this way would his star catalogue be a monument to his own skill and energy and at the same time lend a great reputation to British astronomy. But Flamsteed was not free to make his decisions alone: he was paid from public funds and public opinion should have its way—or so his opponents at the Royal Society argued; and it was they who constituted 'public opinion', since there were few outside who knew about the delays, let alone about the issues involved. The opposition was formidable since it was led by Isaac Newton (1642–1727), then President of the Royal Society.

Newton, whose profoundly important synthesis of planetary and celestial motions we shall come to in the next chapter, was born in 1642 and went up to Cambridge in 1661 as a sizar as his family could not afford the full fees. Here he came under the influence of Isaac Barrow (1630–1677), mathematician and divine, a favourite of Charles II and an inveterate smoker, slovenly in his dress, but impeccable in his scholarship. At first Newton's career at Cambridge was not exceptional, and it was only when he came under Barrow in his third year that his latent genius was recognised. Newton owed a good deal to Barrow, who provided him with a sound training in science, interested him in optics and in every way encouraged a pupil who, within six years, he was to refer to in his *Lectures on Light* as of 'excellent character and of great genius'. But Barrow's greatest tribute lies not in what he said but in what he did, for in 1669 he resigned his chair of mathematics in favour of Newton. What then happened to the undergraduate who had obtained his master degree only two years before? How had he reached such heights in apparently no more than two years?

The truth is that although Newton's progress was slow, it had begun before 1669. Clearly Barrow had awoken all kinds of interests and stimulated a flow of ideas, and these Newton was able to develop alone during the time of the Plague when the university was closed and he was forced to return to his home in Lincolnshire. Here, isolated intellectually, he was able to indulge in his private experiments and his secret thoughts; and although he was only twenty-three it was at this time that, as often happens with mathematicians, he laid the groundwork for all the scientific achievements that were to bring him fame. As he himself later said ' . . . in those days I was in the prime of my age for invention, and minded mathematics and philosophy more than at any time since'.[3] The rural isolation must have suited him, for Newton was always a lone worker who liked to keep his scientific opinions and his scientific results to himself. Indeed, without the persuasions of friends, and here and there the force of circumstance, it seems likely that none of his results would have been published. Reticent to a degree, Newton abhorred the possibility of controversy over claims to scientific priority, and more than once during his career he vowed he would forsake science except, at best, as an occupation for his private satisfaction.

It was while in Lincolnshire that Newton formulated his theory of gravitation and set about making a series of important practical experiments on optics and light. Even as a boy he had been interested in mechanical things, and his practical flair allowed him to set up and successfully carry out a series of experiments with prisms. These showed him that sunlight, or white light, is really a combination of all the colours of the rainbow. Colours were usually explained as the result of different combinations of light and shadow, but Newton's experimental evidence demolished this theory. It also led him to the conclusion that the lens telescopes then in use, which gave images with colour fringes, could never be improved. Although his conclusion was wrong, it led him to design a telescope in which the light was gathered by means of a mirror rather than by a lens, and so was free of the annoying colour fringes. Newton was not the first to think of a reflecting telescope, for James Gregory had suggested the idea in his *Optica Promota* in 1663; but whereas Gregory's theory had never been successfully demonstrated, Newton was able to build himself a very useful instrument.

After long delays the value of the reflecting telescope was recognised, and now in the twentieth century all the large new telescopes are reflectors. For Newton however, although he published nothing about it, it was significant in bringing his work to the attention of the Royal Society in London. With the motto 'nullius in verba', extracted from one of Horace's *Epistles*,[4] the Fellows were enthusiastically living up to the principle of experiment in place of the doctrine of authority, and of taking nobody's word about any new idea without the appropriate evidence to support it: they therefore invited Newton to send his reflecting telescope to London so that they could examine it for themselves. Thus began a long correspondence which led him to publish his views about light and colours and so become embroiled in controversy with some of the ablest scientists at home and abroad. But it brought Newton's name into prominence and he was elected a Fellow of the Royal Society.

Newton's optical work and his invention of a practical reflecting telescope were alone enough to secure him perpetual fame, but his theory of gravitation was his greatest achievement. The results of this work were not published until 1687, when Newton was forty-five, and soon after this he left Cambridge; through connections at Court he was appointed Warden of the Mint and later supervised the great re-coinage that began in 1696.

But if Newton did little in science after his appointment to the Mint and spent most of his leisure time on theology and biblical chronology, there was one scientific matter that did concern him: this was his overriding wish to perfect his theory of the Moon's motion. It was this that led to the trouble with Flamsteed. As early as 1691, five years before he came to London, Newton had urged Flamsteed to publish his results, but since Flamsteed was quite willing to furnish Newton with detailed observations to help him in his work on lunar theory, Newton was not disposed to press his point. In one sense what Flamsteed did with his observations was no one's business provided he himself could obtain what he wanted. Flamsteed even persuaded Newton to sign an undertaking not to divulge the observations and not make known any theory derived from them without his consent, but this was no more than a way of protecting his observations from plagiarism. Only when Flamsteed began to worry Newton about his theory and whether or not he was to receive first intimation of it did their relationship become a little strained. The relationship was not improved by Newton's offer in 1696 to pay Flamsteed for his observations, and by his general treatment of the Astronomer Royal as a servant rather than as a colleague. Flamsteed, a sensitive man, with little tact and never an easy companion, was always touchy about his position, and he took Newton's patronising behaviour as an insult. However, a little later he accepted, apparently wholeheartedly, Newton's somewhat grudging apologies.

But a further factor helped to stir up trouble. Flamsteed had fallen out with Newton's friend and protagonist, Edmond Halley (1656–1742). There seem to have been three reasons for Flamsteed's bitterness towards Halley: in the first place Halley had pointed out to him an error in a paper on the tides around Britain; secondly, and what is more significant, Halley himself observed the Moon and passed observations to Newton, observations which Flamsteed believed to have been stolen from the Royal Observatory. Such behaviour is quite out of keeping with Halley's character, but the incident illustrates well the psychological fear and suspicion under which Flamsteed was living towards the end of the century. Thirdly, Halley and Flamsteed were basically antipathetical in character. Halley was a *bon viveur* whose attitude towards religion was as far from Flamsteed's dour Christianity as can be imagined, and on visits to Greenwich, he sometimes teased Flamsteed for what he took to be his self-righteousness; more than once Flamsteed publicly objected to Halley's 'bantering'. In the light of Flamsteed's growing bitterness, Halley was not inclined to be particularly zealous in trying to dissuade Newton from taking action when the time came.

In 1703 Newton was unanimously elected President of the Royal Society, and after a year in office he decided to brook no more delays in publication from Greenwich. In all fairness, Newton may have thought that publication would be good for both the nation and for Flamsteed, since Queen Anne's consort, Prince George of Denmark, had just been elected a Fellow of the Royal Society and there was every excuse to appeal for funds for what was likely to be an expensive undertaking. Newton persuaded the prince to agree in principle, and then visited Flamsteed about the matter. Flamsteed would not let Newton deal with the publication and prepared a memorandum of his own for the prince. However, purely by chance, the memorandum never reached the prince: it remained at the Royal Society where it so intrigued the Fellows that they immediately set up a committee, with Newton as chairman, to arrange for actual publication. A number of referees, all friends and partisans of Newton, were appointed to supervise and Halley, who had considerable experience as an observer, was given the task of editor. Flamsteed was extremely disgruntled, especially by the fact that the material was to be edited, and he refused to correct the proofs sent to him. He was annoyed that he had been forced to agree to open material which he had sent the referees under seal to await publication later, and even more angry that a Board of Visitors was appointed to inspect the observatory and exercise control over the Astronomer Royal. It was all a most unhappy business, caused partly by Flamsteed's pig-headedness, partly by Newton's magisterial and patronising attitude, and partly by the parsimony of a government that would neither pay its Astronomer Royal an adequate income nor reimburse him for his assistant's help, and steadfastly declined to supply him with instruments for his work. Poor Flamsteed was ill-served, and the fact that he was neither the most co-operative nor ebullient of personalities did not help.

In 1708 Prince George died, but the Committee continued its work and four years later the catalogue appeared under the title *Historia Coelestis*. Flamsteed claimed it was full of errors and he settled down to revising all but the first volume which had received his blessing. Moreover, after the death of Queen Anne in 1714, he persuaded the authorities to send him their stock of 300 of the 400 copies printed and he burned them (all excepting the first volume) 'as a sacrifice to heavenly truth'. Flamsteed died in 1719 but by then the first volume of his own revised *Historia Coelestis Britannica* was completed, appearing in 1725 with two companion volumes nursed along by his faithful assistants Joseph Crosthwait and Abraham Sharp. A catalogue of great accuracy, it brought international fame to Greenwich and contributed towards the reputation for precise observation that the observatory has maintained ever since.

The irony of the situation at Greenwich and of Flamsteed's unhappy rule, was that Edmond Halley, the man whom he quite unjustly called his 'profligate enemy', was appointed as his successor. Halley was then sixty-three and an experienced observer with a long-established reputation, but in spite of his age he set about refurbishing the observatory which once again had few instruments as Flamsteed's widow had taken away those that her husband had bought with his own money.

While he was twenty and still studying at Oxford, Halley had left the university and gone for more than a year to St Helena to observe and catalogue the stars in the southern hemisphere, a task that needed to be done with the improved apparatus (using telescopic sights) available by the 1670's. On his return he was congratulated by the then friendly Flamsteed, who called him the 'southern Tycho'—a great compliment considering the high quality of Tycho Brahe's observations in the northern hemisphere—and after a certain amount of persuasion in the appropriate quarters, Oxford received a royal *mandamus* to grant Halley his M.A., even though he had not kept the proper terms of residence as the regulations demanded.

Halley was a very different character from Flamsteed, who seems to have possessed the unfortunate knack of antagonising the authorities. Halley was far more diplomatic, and when still a young man the Royal Society had asked him to act as their representative in Danzig in an unfortunate dispute which had blown up with Johannes Hevelius (1611–1681), then the doyen of European astronomers. Hevelius, a brewer by trade, had established an elaborate observatory on the roof of his house and was making excellent observations of stellar and planetary positions. However, he would persist in using instruments without telescopic sights, although, when it came to matters of lunar or planetary detail, he was quite happy to make observations with a telescope. Hevelius was attacked by Robert Hooke (1635–1703), at the time one of the honorary secretaries of the Society. Hooke, irascible and, like Flamsteed, not the most tactful of men, was quick of intellect and saw immediately the increase in accuracy possible if telescopic sights were used. Unhappily

Hevelius took Hooke's strictures to be a criticism by the Society itself and there was a considerable amount of ill-feeling. Halley, who used telescopic sights at St. Helena, set out to persuade Hevelius of their value, and it says something for the young man that although he never managed to convince him of the superiority of the telescope for positional measurement, he was able to smooth over the troubles between Hevelius, a man forty-five years his senior, and the Royal Society.

Halley's range of interests was immensely wide, covering archaeology and classical studies, as well as most branches of physical science. His appointment as Astronomer Royal, however was not based on the breadth of his knowledge but on his very real abilities as an astronomer and his desire to solve the problem of longitude. When in his forties, Halley had made an attempt to determine longitude at sea by magnetic observations, his theory being based on the argument that, since a magnetic needle seldom points to the magnetic north but varies from place to place owing to local irregularities in the Earth's crust, it should be possible to determine the precise magnetic variation at any particular place. If, then, the magnetic variation were charted over the oceans, a new means of determining longitude should be available. To this end he was commissioned captain in the Navy and given command of a small ship, the *Paramour*, with orders to chart the magnetic variation over the Atlantic. This he achieved between 1698 and 1700, in spite of mutiny by his second-in-command, who objected to being under the authority of a landsman, and Halley had to navigate and command the ship alone from Barbados to Portsmouth. The subsequent discovery that the variation itself kept changing vitiated his scheme, but did nothing to diminish his reputation; and one positive contribution that came out of his voyage was a method of charting magnetic variations that is still used today.

When Halley took up his duties and had extracted £500 from the government for new equipment, he set about an extensive observing programme. He decided to observe the Moon through the complete eighteen-year period, and fortunately he lived long enough to do this, while among his innovations at Greenwich was a transit instrument, the first ever to be put to regular use. It was a small compact instrument consisting of a telescope free to move only in altitude and mounted facing due south, and for four years Halley used it to time the moment when stars crossed the meridian—a necessary observation for determining stellar positions with real precision. But in 1725 a large wall-mounted quadrant, built by the famous mathematical instrument maker 'honest' George Graham (1675–1751), was ready, and it was with this beautiful instrument that Halley completed his observing programme. It says something for his abilities that in 1731, when only just over half way through the saros, he was able to announce some important preliminary results. After ten years, his observations of the Moon, far more extensive and detailed than any made by Flamsteed, who had concentrated most of his efforts on the stars, showed that it was possible to determine longitude at sea from observations of this kind. The accuracy he could obtain was such as to give the Moon's position correct to within two minutes of arc (one thirtieth part of a degree) and equivalent to an error of only sixty-nine miles at the equator— this was still not close enough for practical use, but was certainly better than any results known at the time and augured well for the future, bringing the problem within sight of a solution.

Halley continued his lunar work, never missing a fine night, so it is said, even though he was now seventy-five, and only when he suffered a slight paralysis in his right hand six years later did he have to curtail his work a little. Even so he did not find it necessary to stop: he did not do so until 1739, when the saros was completed and his health began to fail. He then offered to resign in favour of James Bradley, his own choice as successor, but his resignation was not accepted and Bradley did not take over until Halley's death a little more than two years later. As with Flamsteed, Halley's full observations remained unpublished until after his death, and this in spite of some severe prodding by Newton. But unfortunately they were not as good as Flamsteed's. For some reason Halley never seems to have taken enough care over the minute adjustments that his observing equipment needed, and as will become evident when the new seventeenth- and eighteenth-century theories of the universe are discussed, it was more as a theoretical astronomer that he was important. Yet in the problem of navigation he did show that the sorely needed solution was possible and, as far as Greenwich was concerned, Halley at least saw that it was provided with good instruments that remained its own property. The only thing he was unable to do was to raise the Astronomer Royal's stipend —although, typically, he did manage to increase it in his own case by keeping strong hold of his salary as Savilian Professor of Geometry at Oxford and by persuading Queen Caroline to supplement it by half-pay as a post-captain in the Navy because of his one-time commission on the *Paramour*.

Halley's successor, Bradley (1692–1762), then a man of forty-eight, like Halley had already gained a considerable reputation before he took over Greenwich. His work had been concerned with trying to determine the distance of stars and the fact that his attempts were all unsuccessful was due to the inadequacies in the equipment available to him rather than to anything he lacked as an observer. Although he could obtain no results in his stellar parallax measure, he did make observations that provided the first physical evidence of the Earth's movement through space. But this discovery, coupled with Bradley's measurement of a nodding motion of the Earth's axis, belongs to a different aspect of British astronomy, which will be discussed in Chapter V. Here we are interested in Bradley's contribution to the solution of determining longitude at sea. Observations towards this solution are unlikely to be spectacular unless surrounded by controversy or made as a race against time. But there was no race in Bradley's day: it was purely a matter of refining observations, and with this in mind, in 1742 he began overhauling Halley's equipment and making improvements to the transit instrument in particular.

Bradley appointed his nephew John as assistant at the munificent salary of ten shillings a week, about all he could afford on the still inadequate Greenwich salary. He was a man of principle, and refused the living of Greenwich, which would have substantially increased his income, on the grounds that he could not undertake a cure of souls and attend to the well-being of the observatory at the same time. Fortunately his situation improved, for in 1752, ten years after his appointment, he was awarded a Crown Pension of an additional £250 a year.

In 1748 Bradley extracted the considerable sum of £1,000 from the Admiralty, who acquired the money not from spoiled gunpowder this time, but from the sale of old stores. The funds were used for new instruments made specially by John Bird (*d.*

1776), who, with George Graham's help, had just set up his own business at the 'Sea Quadrant' in the Strand: Bradley's was his first big order. The large quadrant, the first instrument Bird built for Greenwich, was so good that he received orders for duplicates from four large continental observatories, and he supplied a host of smaller versions to amateurs. He built standard yards in 1758 and 1760, manufactured telescopes and even took up observing as a relaxation. Yet in spite of the quality of his work—or perhaps because of it—Bird, like the Astronomer Royal he served, was never a rich man. Bradley was delighted with the new instruments and proceeded to use them to the full. He was a meticulous observer and unlike Halley allowed properly for the inherent errors in his instruments. He accurately observed the positions of more than three thousand stars, and some idea of his care can be seen when it is realised that he not only allowed for the distortion of position caused by the fact that air itself refracts light—Halley had done this—but that he also took into account the temperature and atmospheric pressure, both of which affect the air's density and so its refractive power. Needless to say his observations were astonishingly good, good enough to be of use to astronomers even now.

But the longitude problem was not yet solved, although Bradley's observations were vital raw material for others to work on. At least, they became the raw material after the Board of Longitude won its legal proceedings against Bradley's executor, who insisted that the observations were his own property. Yet even after this battle, the question of ownership of observations was not settled and the same problem cropped up again on the death of Bradley's successor, Nathaniel Bliss (1700–1764), whose eponymous control lasted but two years. Only when Nevil Maskelyne (1732–1811) was appointed as fifth Astronomer Royal in 1765 was the question finally settled: the Board of Longitude stipulated that all observations made at the Royal Observatory were Crown property and should be printed annually at public expense. By then the Board had had enough troubles with the Royal Observatory and wanted peace; but it was not to find it, for during Maskelyne's reign the longitude problem was solved amidst abuse and acrimony.

The Board was established to examine any claims to have

solved the longitude problem and to pay a reward of £20,000, first offered by the British government in 1714 at the instigation of shipping interests in the city of London. The sum was a small fortune in the eighteenth century, and far larger than the Dutch or Spanish government rewards, but it could only be won by an inventor devising some device or method that provided longitude correct to within 30 miles after a six-week voyage. Smaller sums of £10,000 and £15,000 were offered for solutions which gave longitude to within 60 miles and 40 miles. Newton believed that the problem would be solved by some astronomical method and advised the government to this effect, but no limitations were placed on the means that could be devised. The Board of Longitude was immediately established and given powers to supervise the competition and advance small sums for promising methods,—but, typical of British bodies of this kind, only about one third of its members had any conceivable claim to knowing even the rudiments of navigation, let alone the complicated issues involved. Not unexpectedly, the Board acted as a magnet to every wild inventor and crank. They were assailed by one man calling himself John the Baptist, who presented quite irrelevant drawings, by a gentleman from Saxony who claimed he could express various ratios in whole numbers—quite impossible by any means whatever and in any case of no significance in longitude determination—and there were the obviously useless devices like sun dials which had been known from antiquity. But there *were* two promising lines of attack: determining longitude by observations of the Moon—the method of 'lunars' —on which Halley had clearly pinned his faith, and the invention of a really good seafaring clock.

Maskelyne believed that lunar observations would provide the answer and he improved the observatory's equipment and somewhat extended the buildings with a view to obtaining even better results after further observations. One thing that made him so sure that he was right was a trip he had made to St Helena in 1761, four years before his appointment as Astronomer Royal, when he had used the outward and homeward voyages to check the method of lunars and had found it showed great promise; especially since observations were made with a new model of a quadrant devised by John Hadley (d. 1744) some years earlier and based on ideas of Newton and Hooke. Maskelyne had been so successful that two years later he had published his famous *British Mariner's Guide*, a handbook explaining the method and its practical use, and after he became Astronomer Royal he extended this by publishing an annual set of tables that allowed the method of lunars to be used continuously at sea: these, known as the *Nautical Almanac,* first appeared in 1767 and proved so useful that they are still in production. Now, of course, they are not calculated in duplicate by computers working at home, but are produced by electronic computer at the Nautical Almanac office of the Royal Observatory. The immediate success of Maskelyne's method can best be judged from the fact that when in 1781 he produced a special handbook of other tables to be used with the *Nautical Almanac,* 10,000 copies were sold immediately on publication.

Maskelyne's own observations at Greenwich were restricted, on the supposition that it would be better to determine the positions of a few objects with great accuracy than a larger number with less precision. The observations, with all their entries and subsequent calculations carried out in a way precisely laid down by Maskelyne, were made by a staff of assistants, who were continually coming and going until he managed to have their salaries raised from a pittance of £26 a year to £70 and no longer had to find money out of his own pocket to supplement the little that the government paid.

While Bradley, Bliss and Maskelyne were busy with the astronomical solution of the longitude problem, the clockmakers of Britain were trying to evolve the answer in a mechanical fashion, and in 1728, while Halley was still Astronomer Royal, he received a visit from a thirty-five-year-old unapprenticed clockmaker by the name of John Harrison (1693–1776). Harrison had been trained as a carpenter—his father's trade—but had educated himself sufficiently to undertake land-surveying and clockmaking. He brought with him a sample of his 'gridiron' pendulum which automatically compensated for the change in length of a pendulum due to alterations in temperature, and a clock 'escapement' that never required oiling and had a minimal amount of friction: inventions that showed he knew well enough the kind of mechanism needed to develop a timepiece of sufficient accuracy to solve the longitude question. It was fortunate for Harrison that he called on Halley before he went before the

Board, since, as Halley pointed out, the Board would not advance money for mere suggestions. Instead he recommended Harrison to his own instrument maker, George Graham. Graham, a north-countryman like Harrison, bluntly proffered the same advice as Halley—make something that works before going before the Board; but he generously lent Harrison a couple of hundred pounds without any security. Harrison never looked back: he returned to Barrow and set about designing and building a marine timepiece. Six years later it was ready: driven by a double spring, it used his gridiron for temperature compensation, and his own special escapement, and two large weighted bars that looked for all the world like a kind of double pendulum. This was the first marine timekeeper that approached the kind of accuracy required. Harrison tested it on a barge in the Humber and then brought it to London in the spring of 1736. With the Royal Society's support, the Admiralty allowed it to travel with Harrison to Lisbon and back. Although there is no official report of the result there is enough evidence to show that its errors were trifling—a couple of seconds or so—and Harrison was so encouraged by its performance that he moved house to London. Here the clock kept going continuously for the next thirty years without even a break for cleaning and oiling, since Harrison had the foresight to build in his own design of self-lubricating bearings.

With the experience gained, Harrison designed a new, sturdier, but more compact timepiece. Two years later this was ready, but the Board declined to try it at sea since Britain was then at war with Spain and they feared it might fall into enemy hands. This unwitting compliment seems to have pleased Harrison, who thereupon set about building yet another timepiece. This he doubtless intended should be his masterpiece and he lavished fantastic care, ingenuity and affection on it for the next seventeen years. Balance wheels replaced the balance bars; roller bearings, not unlike those in a modern car, and all other possible refinements, were incorporated, and when it was almost ready in 1757 Harrison informed the Board that he intended to compete for the £20,000 prize. He also suggested that he should make a carriage-watch to accompany it as an auxiliary timepiece, and with the Board's blessing he constructed this, his fourth chronometer, with the help of his son. It was in essence a miniature

Nevil Maskelyne, fifth Astronomer Royal; engraving by Edward Scriven from a painting by Vanderburgh in the possession of the Royal Society.

(Ronan Picture Library)

John Harrison, successful inventor of the marine chronometer. His fourth chronometer design, no larger than a pocket watch, is shown on the left. Engraving by William Holl (the younger) after a painting by King.

(Ronan Picture Library)

Isaac Newton: engraving by William Fry from a portrait by Sir Godfrey Kneller.

(Ronan Picture Library)

version of his third timekeeper, the product of seventeen years of work and thought, and was ready six years later. Since it was hardly more than five inches across, whereas timepiece three was the size of a large bracket clock, the watch was the instrument put to the test.

In November 1761 Harrison went on the trial voyage to Jamaica, and when they arrived nine weeks after leaving Portsmouth, the error in longitude was one forty-eighth of a degree, or about one mile. Provided, then, that he could demonstrate to the Board that he had produced a practical and useful instrument—and this he obviously had done—the prize should have been his, but it is here that the Board showed itself less than impartial. They advanced Harrison £2,500, but declined the balance untl they had executed further tests; the precise position of Jamaica, they claimed, was not well enough known to satisfy them. Perhaps they believed that the results were fortuitous for, after all, Newton had claimed it would be impossible to build so good a timepiece; but it is not to their credit that the next trial was delayed for two years. At last, in 1764, Harrison took the timepiece to Barbadoes, accompanied by Maskelyne and an assistant from the observatory, Charles Green. The test was for Maskelyne and the Captain, James Cook, to determine their longitude astronomically at a selected point on Barbadoes and compare their result with that provided by Harrison's timepiece. The results agreed so closely that it was clear the timepiece had an error that worked out at less than one tenth of a second per day.

It was now that the Board's behaviour became disgraceful. First they declined to pay more until Harrison had disclosed the secrets of his timepiece under oath to a committee that included three clockmakers, and had handed over to the Board all four of his timepieces. Even then they were only prepared to part with £7,500 more, and reserved the right to hold the balance of £10,000 until Harrison, now over seventy and with failing eyesight, had made two more timepieces and submitted them to such tests as the Board might devise. Harrison gave his secrets away—there was no other course open to him—and received the £7,500; but for him to build two further timepieces was out of the question, although with his son's help he did manage to construct one more. He felt his cause was lost, especially when

65

Maskelyne issued a bad report after having the watch under test at Greenwich for a year. Aided and abetted by his friend James Short, another instrument maker, and a Fellow of the Royal Society, Harrison attacked Maskelyne's report, impugning Maskelyne's honesty, since he claimed the timepiece could not give longitude correct to within a whole degree after a six-week voyage.

Maskelyne could in a sense be criticised for the tests, in that they were designed to show the timepiece in the least favourable light, while he was known to prefer the method of lunars, and, so it is said, to have disliked Harrison. Yet Maskelyne was probably honest about his results, and the severity of his test may well have been motivated by zeal, even if increased a little by an unhealthy bias against Harrison. In the meantime the Board were not idle. With Harrison's design in their possession they commissioned a well-known clockmaker, Larcum Kendall (1721–1795), to prepare a duplicate of the fourth timepiece; and two years after its completion they sent it out on test with Captain Cook on his second Antarctic voyage. The voyage lasted for three years, from 1772 to 1775, and in spite of the storms and temperature extremes encountered, Cook had only praise for the timepiece and asked specifically for it to be issued to him when he set sail on his third voyage. The Kendall timepiece came through with flying colours, but by then the Board's failure to pay Harrison had rebounded on them and their behaviour was unmasked.

The injustice done to Harrison had come to the ears of George III, the father and son were granted an audience at Windsor where the king listened patiently to their tale. Their fifth timepiece—the only one in their possession—was ordered to be sent to the king's private observatory at Kew. In ten weeks it was in error by $4\frac{1}{2}$ seconds—an average of no more than one twenty-eighth of a second per day—and George III then acted. Harrison was instructed to petition Parliament and questions were asked in the House, questions that Lord North's administration found difficult to answer, and it was decided that there must be a thorough investigation of the Board's actions. This was too much for the Board: they capitulated, and a Bill was passed authorising the payment of the balance to Harrison. Yet still they only paid Harrison a further £8,750, keeping back

£1,250, the amount they had advanced for the construction of his second and third timepieces which he had been forced to hand over to them years before.

By the end of this episode, Maskelyne must have had enough of clockmakers, yet his troubles with them were not over. The Harrison settlement had been made against his will—for he had recommended that half the prize should go to Tobias Mayer's widow for her husband's lunar tables—and now a new storm cloud appeared on the horizon in the form of Thomas Mudge (1716–1794). Mudge had been one of the three clockmakers on the Board's committee which had examined Harrison and received the disclosures of his successful design: a talented and amiable man, he himself began to construct timepieces of great precision following Harrison's design. These were tested by Maskelyne at Greenwich and again, like Harrison's, found wanting, even though they did exceptionally well on a seagoing trial. What is more, Maskelyne seems to have preferred the work of two other clockmakers, so that although Mudge competed three times for the £10,000 prize, he failed each time. This brought down a storm of abuse on Maskelyne, which he weathered as he had weathered the Harrison storm—even though Mudge obtained £2,500 from Parliament in the teeth of strong opposition from the Board.

It is hard to know to what extent Maskelyne was at fault. But if he had a bias against the clockmakers, there is no doubt that he did his work at Greenwich with every care, and his *Nautical Almanac* provided the mariner with a reliable method of longitude determination that was needed as a stand-by however good his chronometer.

Maskelyne died in 1811 at the age of seventy-eight, but the family connection with astronomy continued, for in 1900 Nevil Maskelyne, the great illusionist, made observations at a solar eclipse expedition in North Carolina.

IV

Newton's Law of Gravitation
and the New Universe

GREENWICH OBSERVATORY was established for practical reasons, but it could not be divorced from the purely theoretical side of astronomy and no Astronomer Royal has ever tried to do this. In 1675 when the observatory was founded, the Copernican system had long been established and Kepler's discovery of elliptical orbits was unquestioned—or almost unquestioned. The problem that faced the theoretical astronomer was still to explain the planetary motions and moreover to find the reasons for them, and this no one had succeeded in doing—at least not in any rigorous mathematical way. But the French mathematician and philosopher René Descartes (1596–1650) had made a new synthesis. Taking the basic postulate *'cogito ergo sum'* (I think therefore I exist), and then re-examining the whole philosophical idea of perceiving the physical world, he built up a metaphysical analysis of the nature of material things, such as their extension in space, or the way they could make their presence known. The system he outlined (in the *Principia Philosophiae* published in 1644) was ingenious and logical, and it was Copernican in the sense that it considered the planets to orbit the Sun—but it was wider than this. Each star, Descartes thought, was the centre of a giant whirlpool filled with material substance—indeed his whole universe was a plenum, a packed concourse of material, in which a vacuum had no place. Where the material moved it appeared as bodies that could be observed —stars and planets. Each whirlpool rubbed shoulders with others and the entire universe was a collection of closely packed vortices. On occasions material would, he thought, move from one vortex to another and this was what was observed as a comet. He even went so far as to work out how, once the deity had constructed the universe of matter and motion, the system he devised would evolve.

This Cartesian philosophy had a great following in the mid-seventeenth century and Newton's early scientific notebooks, kept at the instance of his tutor Richard Holdsworth, show that he was thoroughly familiar with it. This is not to say that he agreed with it: indeed it is clear that he questioned many of Descartes' assertions and in some instances preferred the ideas of Pierre Gassendi, another French scientific philosopher; but he was taught, and was intensely interested in, mechanical explanations of how the universe functioned. Newton also paid considerable attention to the mathematical explanations of motion, for the whole problem of planetary behaviour and the construction of the universe was really a problem of moving bodies, since any explanation of the underlying reasons why the planets moved at all depended on ideas of motion. To Aristotle and Ptolemy, and even to Copernicus and Brahe, the planets moved in orbits because this was the essence of their nature. A man is a man because his heart, blood and lungs are in motion: stop them and he is a corpse. In the same way the planets were planets just because they were perpetually in orbit: stop them and they would be fixed like the stars. But Galileo had attacked this attitude, as had others like Giovanni Borelli (1608–1679) and Descartes, and Galileo in particular had made some notable advances which were published towards the end of his life in his *Discorsi ... à due nuove scienze* (*Discourses on two new sciences*). Recent research makes it seem unlikely that Newton ever read this book, but as he was later to give Galileo credit for the work he had done it is clear that he was aware of what Galileo had achieved, and Galileo made it perfectly plain that bodies moved in a way that no scholar of antiquity would ever have admitted, even in his wildest moments. They could, he found, move in two different directions at once: a discovery that made sense of the path of a projectile like a cannon ball which military engineers would persist in believing went first upwards in a straight line, and the plummeted down again in another straight line. Galileo also found that the time bodies take to fall to the ground is the same whether they are heavy or light, and both these discoveries were important cornerstones on which Newton built. Galileo was also quite specific about the motion of a body in a horizontal path—once started, it would keep on going unless something acted on it to stop it. Once again this was a break, and an immense break, with tradition. Previously motion had been supposed to continue only while a body was acted on by a force—in other words a cart would only keep going while the horse was pulling it: stop the horse and the cart stopped too. What Galileo did was to get behind the common sense, everyday explanation and analyse the question further. His horse and cart still behaved as common sense expected, but the reason why was neither so obvious nor so jejune as had previously been believed.

When Newton retired to his home at Woolsthorpe in 1665, the attack on old ideas of motion was well and truly under way. Newton knew very well what had once been believed and what the new ideas were: his work was not done in a vacuum of ignorance, but with a full realisation of current knowledge. Yet this does not detract from his achievement. It simply makes clear that what he did was to distil those facts that were important from a mélange of different ideas and then, with mathematical precision, synthesize them into a completely new universe governed by laws of universal application. Everyone knows the story of how, while Newton was sitting in the garden at Woolsthorpe, turning over in his mind the problem of the Moon's motions, an apple fell at his feet, and gave him the clue he was looking for—the link between the force that caused the apple to fall and the force that caused the Moon to 'fall' towards the Earth so that, instead of following a straight path in space, it continually curved into an orbit round the Earth. The story seems well enough substantiated, but even with such a clue the problem was by no means solved. Newton had to discover the precise effect of gravitation—a term already in use but meaning little more than a mutual 'affection' between bodies that tended to make them unite—and determine how this affection was reduced the further bodies were separated. Then, once he knew this, he must calculate the 'fall' to be expected at the Moon's distance compared with that of, say, an apple from a tree. Finally he needed to compute the amount by which the Moon accelerated along its orbit to produce the precise path observed, and to see whether it agreed with his calculation of the 'fall'—in other words to determine whether the facts really fitted into an explanation that used gravitation as the sole force.

None of this was easy, but Newton did find that a force of gravitation that diminished 'reciprocally as the squares of their distances from the centres about which they revolve ...'[1] answered 'pretty nearly' ($F\alpha$ M_1 M_2/d^2). The design was finished in principle, but not in a form in which he could present it to the world, even supposing that the reticent Newton wanted to do so. He had taken a great stride forward—in a few bold strokes he had sketched out the vast picture of universal gravitation, a picture in which the self-same force was to be seen operating out in space as well as on Earth: but now he must paint in the details, for his own intellectual satisfaction if for no other reason. He had assumed for simplicity's sake that the Moon's orbit was a circle instead of a curve something like an ellipse: a complete theory must make no such assumption, for Newton accepted Kepler's law that planets travel in ellipses, or certainly in orbits close to this shape (unlike some of his contemporaries who doubted the reality of the idea). Newton also had to make sure precisely how gravity operated. If, say, an apple falls, does the force of gravitation which increases the closer the apple approaches the ground, depend on the distance apple to ground or apple to the centre of the Earth? It was no small difference, and a vital one if the theory was to be applied to a comparatively large body like the Moon: Newton had to be sure about it. But the real stumbling block to a complete theory seems to have been the fact that Newton was either unaware of or paid little attention to Kepler's second 'law'—the discovery about the speed of orbital motion at any point—which many astronomers at the time ignored or overlooked.* Thus when he was at Woolsthorpe, his astronomy had not developed enough, and he was not in possession of sufficient facts, to enable him to complete his picture. This had to wait for more than a decade.

Newton was not alone in trying to account for lunar and planetary motions by some kind of law of gravitation. Others

* This is a new explanation of the delay in Newton's completion of his theory, but it seems to me to have much to commend it. It is due to Dr Derek Whiteside and full details are given in the *British Journal for the History of Science*, ii, (December 1966), 117.

were grappling with the problem, but the mathematics involved floored them. They suggested that gravitation operated according to an inverse square law—diminishing reciprocally as the square of the distance as Newton put it—in other words, the power of gravitational attraction diminished by four times if the distance between the attracting bodies (Earth and Moon, Sun and planet) doubled, nine times when it trebled, and so on. But no one was able to prove the fact. It was a problem that exercised the minds of many Fellows of the Royal Society, including the perspicacious Robert Hooke. Hooke was born in 1635 and so was Newton's senior by seven years. He had been one of the founder members of the Society and in 1662 was elected as 'Curator', given apartments in Gresham College, and charged with producing experiments at every weekly meeeting. Born poor and weakly, he grew up into a lean and unprepossessing figure with a sensitivity that made him bad tempered and resentful. For many years Hooke kept turning his attention to the question of planetary orbits and in November 1679 he wrote about the problem to Newton, now well established as Lucasian professor of mathematics at Cambridge. This was not their first contact, for some years earlier they had crossed swords over the nature of light on which Newton held very different ideas from those generally accepted. In 1679 Hooke was one of the Secretaries of the Royal Society, so his peace overtures could be shrouded in a polite invitation asking Newton to 'continue your former favours to the Society by communicating what shall occur to you that is philosophicall, and in returne I shall be sure to acquaint you with what we shall Receive.... And you may be assured that whatever shall be soe communicated shall be noe otherwise farther imported or disposed of then you yourself shall prescribe. I am not ignorant that both heretofore and not long since also there have been some who have indeavoured to misrepresent me to you and possibly they or others have not been wanting to doe the like to me, but Difference in opinion if such there be (especially in Philosophicall matters ...) me thinks should not be the occasion of Enmity—tis not with me I am sure.'[2]

Having thus placed everything on a friendly footing Hooke goes on to ask Newton his 'thoughts' about planetary motions. In particular he mentions motion directly along the orbit combined with the effect of 'an attractive motion towards the central body', and seeks Newton's opinion on this. Newton was obviously surprised and tried to deflect Hooke's attention to something else, since he had not then proved his own ideas conclusively. Instead he wrote about the Earth's rotation and discussed the path taken by a body falling from a great height— not quite such an irrelevancy as it might seem, for Hooke had published a book, *Attempt to prove the motion of the Earth by Observation,* five years before. But Hooke was not to be diverted from his purpose and turned the correspondence back to his first question by arguing over Newton's conclusions about the falling body and pointing out how the two problems were related. Newton replied about falling bodies again, Hooke returned to his original question: it was clear that Newton could no longer side-step the issue, so he wrote no more to Hooke but once more turned his attention to celestial motions.

No one can say what Newton would have done if he had not been prodded from outside—probably he would have sat tight and kept his solution to himself. Even so, it was another five years before anything happened and then, in January 1684, Wren, Hooke and Halley met, as they often did, at a coffee house, and fell to discussing the problem. Halley claimed that an inverse square law of gravitation fitted well with Kepler's third law that connected the time a planet took to orbit and its distance from the Sun, but he could go no further. In particular he could not mathematically link up the type of orbit with gravitation, although he had a definite feeling that this ought to be possible. Wren said that he was close on Halley's heels but, again, had come up against a brick wall. Hooke, on the other hand, claimed that he had arrived at a complete answer to all planetary motions based on the inverse square law; knowing Hooke and his claims—often justified, but often not—Wren offered a valuable book to whoever was the first to bring along a solution. Halley was unable to do so and Hooke procrastinated, and in August Halley, while on a visit to Cambridge, went to see Newton and discussed the problem with him. Newton's answer was immediate and surprising: he had, he said, worked out the whole thing but had then thrown it aside, being in the midst of some other investigation that had taken his fancy. Newton then tried to produce the relevant papers but they could not be found, so he promised to rework the mathematics and send the results to Halley: he was as good as his word and in November the material arrived.

It is fortunate that it was sent to Halley. If it had gone to Wren it might have received the prize but no more, if to Hooke there would doubtless have been arguments about this point or that; but Halley, a very good mathematician, not only found that Wren's problem had been solved—he had the perception to see that here was something far more significant. Newton had produced the concept of *universal* gravitation since he had linked terrestrial gravity with celestial gravity—falling bodies on Earth with falling bodies in space. Halley visited Newton post haste, discussed the question of further investigations and urged Newton to send his results to the Royal Society so that their receipt might be registered and Newton's priority established. Halley seems to have gained Newton's complete confidence—no easy task—and in December at the Royal Society meeting, Halley reported what had transpired; he and a friend, Edward Paget (1656–1703?) were then charged with keeping Newton in mind of his promise to deliver complete details. In due course the first part of Newton's complete theory was delivered and even a cursory examination showed how valuable it was: it showed, too, that there was no sense in trying to publish it in the Society's scientific journal *Philosophical Transactions* and that the only possible course was for the Society to publish it as a book. This was not an unusual undertaking for them: they had already published a book by Hooke, one by John Evelyn (1620–1706), the posthumous works of Horrox, and a host of other volumes. In principle the idea was admirable, but in practice it was not so good since they were in financial difficulties. Some books had not sold well, subscriptions were in arrears and, in the event, Halley himself undertook to pay the printer as well as edit the book. Newton was never to forget this generosity, and the two men remained friends until his death, in spite of the disparity of their characters.

Newton's work did not run smoothly. The printers were slow and Halley had to employ more than one, but the real stumbling block was Robert Hooke. The trouble began in the early summer of 1686, when Halley sent a letter to Newton about his 'incomparable treatise'.[3] 'There is one thing more,' he wrote, 'that I ought to informe you of, viz, that Mr Hook has some pretensions upon the invention of ye rule of the decrease of Gravity, being reciprocally as the squares of the distances from the Center. He sais you had the notion from him, though he owns the Demonstration of the Curves generated thereby to be wholly your own; how much of this is so, you know best, ...' Hooke wanted a mention in the preface and this, one can only feel, would have been a nice gesture, even if not completely justified. But Newton did not agree. 'In the papers in your hands,' he replied to Halley,[4] 'there is noe one proposition to which he can pretend, & soe I had noe proper occasion of mentioning him there. In those behind where I state the systeme of the world, I mention him and others.' In other words, when it came to a specific explanation of the rotation of the Earth and falling bodies on it, Hooke would get his just deserts, but not in the beginning of the book in which the basic laws of motion were stated and analysed. Not only was Newton adamant; he gave Halley a long and detailed explanation of what he remembered of the whole business, pointing out that Wren knew the law as well as Hooke, although he did unbend enough to say that if Hooke thought otherwise he might put him in mind of it. But Hooke was not satisfied and it seems that he created a great fuss at one of the Royal Society's meetings, claiming that he had supplied everything Newton had written—or words to that effect. This was reported to Newton 'by one who had it from another lately present at one of your meetings',[5] and a blast to Halley followed. Hooke's inability to deal with the problem is stressed by Newton in no uncertain terms and this, of course, was true enough. Halley and Wren could not find a solution either and it was only Newton with his rare mathematical flair and the ability to discipline himself to carry through the tedious work of arithmetical calculations who had supplied the proof. Newton was willing to mention Hooke in the appropriate place, but nowhere else; at least he was until it was reported to him that Hooke's claims were growing wilder and more demanding, for he then decided he would not finish the third part of his 'divine treatise', the part in which Hooke was to be named. It needed all Halley's diplomacy to calm Newton but he did manage to and, in July 1687, the great *Philosophiae Naturalis Principia Mathematica* (*Mathematical Principles of Natural Philosophy*) was at last published, complete with the last part which was really the crowning glory of the work.

The *Principia* has been called the greatest product of the human intellect, but such praise is disproportionate. Yet it was a work of supreme importance that affected the whole of science by its logic and its breadth, the astounding powers of mathematical analysis it displayed, and the clarity of its text. In its three books Newton runs the whole gamut of physical science in its application to the seventeenth-century universe. Beginning with an enunciation of three laws of motion which were an extension of Galileo's work and broke away completely from the ideas of Aristotle and of the medieval philosophers, the first book continues with the way in which multiple forces operate together—the first really clear formulation ever made of this confusing problem—the impact of one body on another, and the law of universal gravitation. This alone would have made Newton's name remembered for as long as dynamics, the physical study of motion continues, but the theme is developed further in book two. Here Newton concerns himself with what happens when motion takes place through a resisting medium such as water or air, and this allows him to support Galielo and explode in even greater detail the old belief that bodies of different heaviness fall at different speeds—a vitally important point if his concept of universal gravitation was to stand against all criticism. In book three, subtitled the *System of the World,* Newton went on to apply the principles laid down in the first two books. Here his laws of motion are used to explain the orbits of the satellites round Jupiter that Galileo discovered, the orbits of the planets round the Sun, taking into account Kepler's three laws (or, rather, showing how they are a natural consequence of the law of universal gravitation); and then he turns to the Earth itself. Here its daily rotation, the movement of its axis in space and its shape are discussed; this is followed by an explanation of how the gravitational pull of the Sun and Moon cause the tides. The book ends with a study, as far as Newton could then take it, of the precise motion of the Moon.

This tremendous *tour de force* was, of course, at first comprehensible to only a few, even of those who could read Latin. Newton himself spoke of it as a 'hard book', even though his mathematics was achieved by geometry rather than the calculus that he had developed and which, although more appropriate, would only have created another difficulty for the reader. All the same, in spite of its difficulty the book aroused great interest, especially in Britain where the scientifically minded were not the only readers, or at least not the only ones who attempted to read it. Literary men tried, and it is said that one nobleman even paid a tutor fifty guineas to help him with the mathematics. The philosopher John Locke (1632–1704) discussed the soundness of Newton's work with the great Dutch physicist Christiaan Huygens (1621–1695) and when it received Huygens' blessing, settled down to read the less mathematical sections; while Richard Bentley (1662–1742), cleric and classical scholar who within five years of publication was to give a series of lectures on the follies of atheism, consulted Newton about the support he wished to derive from the theories in the *Principia*. Unfortunately Bentley's later career did not live up to the brilliance of his lectures: he was arrogant, argumentative and not a little avaricious, and when many years later Newton was asked why on earth he had let Bentley print the second edition, part of which appeared in 1710, he replied that Bentley was covetous and that he was allowed to do it for the money. Strangely enough Newton, who was not above wanting good remuneration for what he did, never made any money for himself out of the *Principia*. The first edition sold out and such profits as there were went into Halley's pocket, money from the second edition went to Bentley, and from the third to its editor Henry Pemberton (1694–1771). The avaricious Bentley did not give a penny to Roger Cotes (1682–1716), the editor of the second edition, a brilliant young man who died at the age of thirty-four.

But if the *Principia* went into three editions, that is not to say that this new synthesis was welcomed everywhere—or even accepted. In France in particular, the Cartesian system was still cherished, and Newton's explanation of everything by a mysterious universal force of gravitation was even considered as a retrograde step; Descartes' universe full of matter whirling in vortices was, they were certain, to be preferred to a strange force that operated with mathematical precision but otherwise appeared intangible. Obscurantist though such a preference may seem today now that we are wise after the event, there was something to be said for it at the time. Newton very carefully did not commit himself about the nature of gravitation. In the first book of the *Principia* he wrote, 'For I here design only to give a Mathematicall notion of those forces, without considering their Physical causes and seats', and all along he studiously avoided proposing any hypothesis that could not be demonstrated by observation and experiment. He concerned himself with the behaviour of bodies since this could be observed and was susceptible to experiment, but he eschewed the nature of the force that *caused* this behaviour, because it was impossible to observe directly or determine from experimental evidence. And Newton kept to this opinion, in spite of criticism and temptations to venture into the arena of speculation. In a letter to Bentley six years after the *Principia* was first published, Newton wrote, 'You sometimes speak of gravity as essential & inherent to matter: pray do not ascribe that notion to me, for ye cause of gravity is what I do not pretend to know...'[6] The new universe of the *Principia*, then, was something to be accepted as a mathematically proved synthesis of planetary behaviour; it was emphatically not an insight into their physical nature.

The French continued to reject Newton's synthesis for a long time and the theory only began to take root in France when Voltaire introduced the general principles, shorn of their mathematics, in his *Lettres Philosophiques* published at Paris in 1765, nearly forty years after Newton's death. What had really been required was obviously either some basic explanation of the nature of gravitation—something that still eludes even the twentieth-century astronomer—or an astronomical event that could only have been predicted by way of Newtonian theory. Such an event, predicted, more than half a century earlier from the principles laid down by Newton, occurred on Christmas Day, 1758.

Appropriately enough its author was Edmond Halley. Halley was the first to apply Newton's doctrines to a practical astronomical problem, and the one that was intriguing him at about this time was the question of cometary paths. These were difficult to decide upon and were a continual source of argument among astronomers—such a challenge was just the kind of thing that Halley could not pass by. The problem lay in the fact that a comet could—and still can—only be observed when comparatively close to the Sun: only then is it bright enough to be visible even through a telescope. The physical reason for this we now know is due to solar influence: when a comet, which is a collection of lumps of rock and frozen gas, is close to the Sun some of its material vaporises and glows due to the strength of solar radiation, but at more than a comparatively short distance off, the radiation it receives is not strong enough to have such effects. In Halley's and Newton's day, the physical nature of comets was not understood, but astronomers were well aware that they were only observed when near the Sun and herein lay their difficulty. Sometimes comets appeared to travel in straight lines, but on most occasions they seemed to have paths that could quite easily be either ellipses, parabolas, or hyperbolas. These curves were well known from the classic work on 'conic sections' by Apollonios in the third century B.C., who had discovered that all three could be formed by cutting a cone in various ways and had therefore proved, geometrically speaking, that all showed certain family resemblances. The main difference between an ellipse and its two sister curves is that they are open while it is closed; or, to put it another way, something travelling in an ellipse will return time and again, but if its path is a hyperbola or parabola it will be seen only once. Since they were not very frequent, comets were considered to be visitors that came close to the Sun once in their lifetime and the question of their reappearance did not arise. Newton had considered cometary orbits in book three of the *Principia*, but while he had proved that, according to his theory of universal gravitation, they must travel in one of the three conic section curves he had not be able to prove which one, and had come down in favour of a parabola.

Halley made a very thorough investigation of the matter, collecting all available cometary observations and then carrying out long and tedious computations to try which of the three curves best fitted the observed paths. Comets could, he discovered, orbit round the Sun in any direction and approach it at all kinds of angles, thus differing substantially from planets, which always orbit in the same direction and nearly all approach the Sun at almost the same angle. He found, too, that as far as he could ascertain, no comet moved with a great enough velocity to give it a hyperbolic path after approaching the Sun, and his problem was reduced to deciding between an ellipse and a parabola. In September 1682 a bright comet had appeared and Halley took its observed positions and from them computed an elliptical orbit, which seemed to give a period of about seventy-five years for its return. Further study led him to connect this with bright comets that had appeared in 1607 and 1531, and an application of Newton's gravitational theory caused him to calculate the way in which the giant planets Jupiter and Saturn would affect the path by virtue of their own attractions—a factor which had not previously been considered, but one of vital importance for a narrow oval orbit such as he found a comet to possess. In 1705 he published his results in the *Philosophical Transactions* and came to what was to be an epoch-making conclusion—that the comet would return in 1758. This paper, *Astronomiae Cometicae Synopsis* (Synopsis of Cometary Astronomy) created a considerable stir, but its prediction of the return of the 1682 comet had to wait for confirmation. Halley himself became increasingly confident in his conclusion and when the 'Synopsis' was reprinted as an addendum to his astronomical tables, which appeared posthumously in 1752, it contained an identification of the comet with those that had appeared in 1456, 1380 and 1305, accompanied by the following comment: 'wherefore if according to what we have already said it should return again about the year 1758, candid posterity will not refuse to acknowledge that this was first discovered by an Englishman.'[7] Halley was correct. In December 1758 the comet did reappear, even though Jupiter's perturbing effect had not been quite as he had computed it, and the theory of universal gravitation had at last received independent confirmation.

In 1717 Halley had also observed a dim comet with his telescope and this was again the first recorded instance of such an observation. But the most significant thing about his cometary work, besides the independent support it gave to the theory enshrined in the *Principia*, was that it finally swept away the superstitious dread that had been attached to comets. In a sense this had been natural enough when the current belief was that a comet was caused by incandescent vapours in the Earth's atmosphere, for with the doctrine of the bodily humours and the conception of the Aristotelian qualities 'hot', 'dry', 'wet' and 'cold' that were believed to have a direct effect on health, a fiery body in the air might well be expected to produce those meteorological conditions so frequently associated with disease and pestilence. Perhaps this ought to have disappeared earlier, when Tycho Brahe conclusively showed that a comet which appeared in 1577 lay beyond the 'sphere' of the Moon, but the apparently capricious way in which comets came and went was still enough to lend authority to superstition. Halley's hard-headed mathematical analysis was needed before the belief in comets as evil omens and harbingers of epidemics could be exorcised, and even so this had to wait until his prediction was confirmed.

With the publication of the *Principia* and its assimilation which followed over the years, the age-old problem of accounting for planetary motions was solved. No longer had the astronomer to rack his brains and make his way through months of tedious calculation in order to find some way to 'save the phenomena'. This had now been done once and for all. A basic theory of planetary motion had been established, a theory that made a complete synthesis with terrestrial phenomena as well. It was time to turn to other fields for conquest, and it is interesting that it was Halley himself who began the adventure away from the local area of the planetary system when he turned his attention to the depths of space, the nature of which Thomas Digges had guessed at nearly a century and a half before.

Halley was a pioneer in stellar astronomy, and carried out most of his work in this field in the five years, 1715 to 1720, just before he was appointed Astronomer Royal. His first significant results appeared in 1715 with a paper in the *Philosophical Transactions* on variable stars and novae. Some of this records results of his own observations and part is concerned with a résumé of the work of others. He discusses the ordinary kind of variable star, goes into some detail about four notable examples, and then draws the conclusion that the novae, like the one observed by Brahe and Digges, are essentially a different kind of object from the ordinary variable. This was a sound observation and one that stimulated other work later on, particularly by William Herschel (1738–1822) and John Goodricke (1764–1785), an incredibly intelligent deaf-mute. Goodricke, working around 1784, discovered not only variation but, in the specific case of

81

the star Algol, found that it varied in a perfectly regular way, and suggested that it was perhaps periodically eclipsed by a dimmer companion star passing in front of it and so cutting out its light, a suggestion that was confirmed a century later.

But Halley did not confine himself to variable stars and novae: everything in the heavens was the object of his curiosity and he spent some time studying the hazy patches of starlight that can be seen in plenty with binoculars or a small telescope and a few of which are visible to the naked eye. Galileo in 1609 had discovered that the hazy band of the Milky Way was really no more than a vast concourse of separate stars; but Halley, after examining a number of telescopic cloudy patches or 'nebulae', came to the conclusion that he was certainly not looking at stars 'but in reality [they] are nothing else but the Light coming from an extraordinary great Space in the Ether; thro' which a lucid Medium is diffused, that shines with its own proper Lustre'.[8] We know now that there are indeed immense glowing gas clouds in space but in Halley's day space—his Ether—was occupied by planets, comets and stars. Certainly others had observed nebulae and had noted them down, but it was left to Halley to analyse the results. It is interesting, too, that he conjectured that the 'extraordinary great Space' each occupied was probably as large as the whole planetary system. This was a broad sweep of the imagination and although in fact it underestimates their size, it was a bold interpretation to have placed on his observations. Again, as in the case of his variable star conclusions, this was to act as a lead to other astronomers at home and abroad, and set them securely on the path of stellar astronomy.

Perhaps the most unusual result of this voyage into interstellar space that Halley took with his small but obviously efficient telescope, was his discovery that the stars, believed since the earliest times to be fixed permanently in position, did not behave in this way at all: they moved. It was a small movement only, and hard to detect, but there was no doubt of its reality. The perpetual unchanging universe of stars, each in its ordained place, was a myth, fathered on astronomy because of the inability of previous observers in the days before the telescope to measure position sufficiently well to detect such minute motions. It was so well accepted a belief that it might have remained unquestioned even by Halley, had it not been for the particular interest he also had in cataloguing star positions. It was known that these appear to change due to the 'precession' or motion of the Earth's axis, a motion which could be explained by gravitation and which Newton had discussed in the third book of the *Principia*: it was checking this theory that aroused Halley's interest and made him want to redetermine the motion in precise terms. To achieve his object Halley examined the star positions catalogued by Hipparchos in the second century B.C., those determined by Ptolemy in the second century A.D., and those he had himself measured. He found, as he expected, that there was an apparent shift of position over the previous 1,800 years, and this allowed him to compute the amount of precession.

But for stellar astronomy the significant thing was that Halley discovered another and quite unexpected shift in the positions of three bright stars. This was, it is true, a far smaller shift than that caused by precession—it was no more than one third of a degree—but he had no doubt about its validity: it was a shift which, though small, was far in excess of any errors in measurement, even in the time of Hipparchos. A study of measurements made earlier by Timocharis in Alexandria showed that the shift over yet another century and a half was even greater. 'It is scarce credible that the Antients could be deceived in so plain a matter, the three Observers confirming each other', Halley wrote, and he followed his hunch that this meant '. . . these stars, being the most conspicuous in Heaven, are in all probability the nearest to the Earth, and if they have any particular Motion of their own, it is most likely to be perceived in them, which in so long a time as 1800 Years may shew itself by the alteration of their places, though it be utterly imperceptible in the space of a single Century of Years.'[9] It would have been more accurate if Halley had referred to the three stars he was concerned with as among the most conspicuous in the heavens, but his conclusion was sound enough and revolutionary in what it suggested. Nevertheless, there was little work done to confirm or deny Halley's theory, primarily because a far higher standard of accuracy was required before this could even be attempted, an accuracy in positional observation that no one could achieve before there were many refinements of technique. In one sense at least, Halley's discovery of the 'proper motion' of the stars was ahead of its time.

In the *Principia* the theory of universal gravitation was confined to the planetary system; could it be applied further? It was accepted, in Britain at least, that the stars extended to great distances in space, but did the inverse square law operate over such vast expanses of the universe? Was it a truly universal law? Doubtless Newton himself had considered the matter, but it seems first to have been raised in an indirect manner by Richard Bentley when he was preparing his lectures against atheism. Bentley wanted to know whether the stars extended limitlessly through space or were only spread out in a comparatively local way: not because he was concerned with the scientific consequences, but because he wanted to establish evidence of a divine creation. Newton answered that in his opinion, if the universe of stars were finite, and the stars evenly distributed throughout it, with the proviso that every particle of matter possessed a gravitational attraction for every other, then everything ought to gravitate together forming one vast spherical globe. Since, quite obviously, this was not the case, the universe must be infinite with the stars distributed throughout it. As far as creation itself was concerned, Newton supposed that the Sun and stars were formed from 'lucid' matter, while the planets required dark matter suitable for bodies that shine only because they reflect sunlight, and it was his opinion that such a selection of suitable material required divine intervention. Newton's view was given to Bentley in private correspondence, but the lectures or 'sermons' as Bentley called them, were published in 1693, and it is quite likely that Halley discussed the astronomical consequences with Newton. At any rate, in 1720 Halley considered the question and, in particular, what an infinite universe of stars ought to look like. On the face of it, if there were an infinite number of stars extending without limit into space, then the whole of the sky ought to be covered by stars and the sky should always appear bright. Evidently this was not so and some explanation had to be found.

Halley's solution was that the sky appeared dark because the brightness of stars drops off more rapidly in proportion to their distance, so making many intrinsically invisible. To support his argument he pointed out that the larger a telescope, the more stars are seen; the obvious corollary being that the light of very distant stars is too weak to have any effect on the eye when it reaches us. In his paper on the subject in *Philosophical Transactions*,[10] there is a flaw in the mathematics of Halley's argument, but this is a minor matter: here was the first attempt to analyse rationally the distribution of stars throughout the entire universe. The problem was tackled a century later by Heinrich Olbers (1758–1840), who found Halley's mistake, and showed that the darkness of the night sky still remained a paradox. This is known as 'Olbers' paradox', and it has only been possible to solve it with the kind of observational equipment that has become available in the twentieth century, coupled with modern interpretations of the observations.

In his own day Halley had a most enviable reputation and it seems clear from what his contemporaries said of him that if it had not been for Newton, he would have been the most respected astronomer of his generation. His influence on later generations was extensive, but it was some time before his pioneer work in stellar astronomy began to have its effect. A popular astronomical book by his friend John Keill (1671–1721), which ran into many editions, mentions neither Halley's speculations about infinite space, nor his ideas about the nebulae, and even neglects his important discovery of the proper motion of the stars. Yet John Keill was a mathematician and professor of astronomy at Oxford, and was fully qualified to understand and interpret the new investigations. He seems to have been content to describe the restricted universe of Sun, Moon and planets, to mention the theory of gravitation, and to leave his readers there, settled in the cosy confines of a small arena where universal gravitation could have its eternal sway and nothing outside should be allowed to disturb the peace. Another well known astronomical book of the period, by the quack physician John Hill (1716–1775), was also silent about the new stellar discoveries. Indeed for many decades little seemed to be done except at Greenwich Observatory, where some valuable results of precise measurement were achieved.

Elsewhere in the country there was a lethargy, most astronomers seemingly knocked into insensibility by the magnitude of Newton's synthesis. It was no doubt the undue reverence for Newton, which led Pope to write his execrable couplet—

'Nature and Nature's laws lay hid in night:
God said, *Let Newton be!* and all was light'

—and Cowper to speak of Newton as a 'childlike sage', that for
many years had the effect of a dead hand on critical studies, with
everyone seemingly content merely to extol Newton as a saint
and interpret his science without an original thought of their own.
In mathematical astronomy this was to be more than a passing
phase and had unhappy consequences, arising from the acrimony
over the invention of the calculus which around 1712 grew into
a storm that embroiled the Royal Society.

There is no need to go into the trouble in detail. It was a
complex affair that brought little credit to the German Gott-
fried Leibniz (1646–1716), whose claims to the invention were
sound enough, and less still to Newton and a clique of British
mathematicians and astronomers who wished all the credit for
Newton. It was one of those tedious disputes over priority about
a discovery that had been made independently by two different
people, and seems to have begun in earnest because of a hatred
for Leibniz cherished by a young Swiss mathematician, Nicolas
Fatio de Duillier (1664–1753). Twenty-two years Newton's
junior, he had come to England to live in 1687. On a visit to
the Continent a couple of years later he met Leibniz and they
discussed the calculus, since both were struggling to develop it
into a powerful mathematical tool designed to deal with quantities that were continually in a state of flux, quantities such as
those that describe the motions of the planets. It seems that
Leibniz took a rather patronising attitude towards Fatio and his
work—he was nearly twenty years Fatio's senior—and it is
certain that the young man believed he was despised: on his
return to England he determined to have his revenge. He became
so much one of Newton's intimates that he was considered as
editor for a subsequent edition of the *Principia*, and he almost
persuaded Newton to join the French mystical and extremist
Protestant sect of Camisards of which he was an ardent
supporter.

The first broadside in the battle was fired by Fatio in a tract
on motion of bodies in a resisting medium, the basic principles
of which were in the second book of the *Principia*, and which
appeared in 1699. Here he stated that he used the calculus which

he had invented by his own exertions, and then viciously abused Leibniz and his 'unremitting vanity'. Fatio next explained that he had found that neither he nor Leibniz was the real inventor —that the credit was Newton's. But the trouble lay in the fact that Fatio accused Leibniz of having stolen Newton's ideas. How much Newton was privy to the attack is unknown, but the fight was on. Leibniz was indignant and pointed to the fact that in the *Principia* Newton had acknowledged the independence of his (Leibniz's) invention: Newton, he claimed, would vindicate him. But Newton remained silent and his silence was taken as condemnation. Leibniz then wrote a defence in a Leipzig scientific journal, the editors of which refused Fatio the right of reply on the grounds that the publication was not a suitable medium for controversy.

For almost five years things were quiet and only flared up again in 1704, when Newton published his *Opticks*. Although it was primarily concerned with his theories of light and colours, two mathematical texts were added, and in the preface Newton wrote, 'In a letter written to Mr *Leibnitz* in the year 1679 ... I mention'd a Method by which I had found some general Theorems about squaring Carvilinear Figures ... [i.e., the calculus]. And some years ago I lent out a Manuscript containing such Theorems, and having since met with some Things copied out of it, I have on this Occasion made it publick ...' Obviously Newton was now persuaded, justly or unjustly, and doubtless after much prodding from Fatio, that on his visit to England in 1673 Leibniz had learned more than Newton had previously realised. Fatio, Keill and another friend, Joseph Raphson, first led the attack, but now Newton himself had assumed command. Leibniz counter-attacked, writing an anonymous review of Newton's two tracts and, to all intents and purposes, accusing Newton of plagiarism. There was another uneasy silence, broken three years later by Keill. Things now went from bad to worse and the Royal Society set up a committee to provide what was ostensibly to be an unbiased report. Newton claimed the committee was international in membership, although of its eleven members only two were foreigners and only one of these had any mathematical knowledge, the rest of the committee consisting of friends of Newton or Keill. The committee never invited Leibniz either to defend himself or to produce documentary evidence. Their findings were what we should expect: they upheld Newton as the discoverer of 'fluxions' as he called the calculus—a correct enough conclusion in all conscience, since as early as 1666 Newton had laid down the foundations of the idea—but they did nothing to exonerate Leibniz as a possible independent discoverer. Newton's slur of plagiarism remained.

Newton had directed the committee's labours by choosing documents and supplying them with interpretations and, worse still, there were political overtones, since the Tories were keen to prevent a Hanoverian succession and at least one member of the committee, Halley, was an avowed Tory: blackening the character of Leibniz would materially assist their cause. Needless to say the committee's report failed to clear up anything and bickering continued, and the trouble reached the level where foreign ministers and ambassadors were invited to the Royal Society to examine the documents—which, of course, they found inconclusive. Newton was prevailed upon to write to Leibniz himself, but his letter did little more than tell Leibniz that he should prove his contentions since he had started the controversy —hardly a proposal that was likely to bring about a rapprochement. Leibniz died suddenly late in 1716, but even after this there were a few salvos fired in Newton's vindication.

The Newton-Leibniz controversy has been termed the most famous of all battles about the priority of a scientific discovery, and there is no doubt that it was. Newton came out of it apparently unscathed; and although modern studies of the whole unhappy business have not left his name unsmeared, his apparently complete vindication at the time had the most unfortunate effect on eighteenth-century British astronomy. Leibniz's scheme of mathematical notation was cast aside by all British mathematicians and that devised by Newton was unreservedly accepted, and while this may seem to be no great matter, it was, in fact, of considerable significance. In the calculus, as in other developments of more advanced mathematics, the signs and symbols that the mathematician uses act as a guide to the operations he is performing; they are a language which makes clear to him precisely what is happening at every stage. If the symbolism, notation, or whatever we are to call it, is obscure, or less specific than it might be, another mental process of interpretation is needed and this is bound to absorb some of his attention. In the case of the calculus there is no doubt that Leibniz's notation was far and away more descriptive than Newton's. By cutting themselves off from anything to do with the 'plagiarist' Leibniz, British mathematicians were forced to adopt Newton's methods and, as the years went by, progress was slowed down. No such brake was put on continental mathematicians, many of whom quite rightly felt that Leibniz had been wronged, and who wholeheartedly adopted his notation, never turning back to Newtonian symbolism. As a result it was not in Britain that Newton's universal gravitation was developed to account for every minute disturbance of planetary motion, but on the Continent, particularly in France. The impetus moved across the Channel and remained there for more than a century after Newton's death.

Fortunately the shift of mathematical astronomy from Britain did not leave the country barren: there was progress, but it lay in other fields free from an atmosphere of personal abuse and wrangling over priorities. One of these was the speculation on the structure of the universe, a side of astronomy which was to prove full of exciting possibilities and one which was later to grow into a preoccupation for many astronomers the world over. However, in the eighteenth century it was a new venture that was triggered off by the problem of the Milky Way.

Galileo had discovered that the Milky Way was composed of stars, but for a long time no one discussed the reason why it stretched right round the heavens, or had drawn conclusions from what was evidently a strange phenomenon if the stars are to be thought of as extending regularly and infinitely out into the depths of space. The first scientific speculations about it seem to have come from William Derham (1657–1735), a friend of Halley's, a cleric and a notable solar observer. While Halley was busy with his investigations of stellar distribution, Derham published his book *Astro-Theology*, which married together his calling as a priest and his persuasion as a scientist. It ran into many editions and to these Derham added a note in which he refers to his own observations of the Milky Way which suggested to him novel ideas. These were that there were more novae to be found in the 'Galaxy', as he called it, that its apparent whiteness was due partly to light reflected from many planets orbiting round the stars which composed it, and that even the stars composing it were in motion. In one sense these comments were wild—at least they appear so in the light of later research—but they do show that the Galaxy was at last receiving attention, which later was to prove extremely worthwhile. Derham's book was popular, and one reader whom it stimulated to make an independent and very different investigation was a north-country teacher of navigation, Thomas Wright (1711–1786).

Wright made observations through a small reflecting telescope and pondered the layout as well as the contents of the Galaxy. That it extended right round the heavens, being seen as an endless belt of stars whether observed from the northern or southern hemisphere, was well known, and the obvious suggestion had been made that it was a ring of distant stars. But to Wright this seemed to smack too much of a hideous asymmetry in the heavens. His strongly religious temperament revolted against a view so aesthetically unsatisfactory and clearly unlikely to be the way chosen by a divine creator: moreover it did not really make sense of the concept of an infinite universe about which Newton and Halley had expressed no doubts whatsoever. After due consideration, and taking into account the observed fact that the stars in the rest of the sky are distributed far more sparsely than in the narrow band of the Galaxy, Wright suggested that the Sun was the centre of the stellar system and that by far the greatest majority of the stars were distributed in the form of a giant disk extending infinitely outwards. The idea that the Sun was at the centre was obvious enough and supported the belief that the stars were closer together, at least in the Milky Way, than even the nearest was to the Sun; to consider it in glorious isolation was logical enough if grossly mistaken. But Wright's suggestion of an infinite disk of stars was far more novel, as too was his idea that the cloudy nebulae were *other* star systems, possibly akin to the Sun and the Milky Way system. Unfortunately Wright's book, *An Original Theory or New Hypothesis of the Universe*, seems to have been little read, although a summary of it did appear in a German periodical and served to make the great Immanuel Kant (1742–1804) (in his *Allgemeine Naturgeschichte* of 1755) put forward a hypothesis along Wright's lines, which in addition contained an ingenious theory of the origin of the universe based on gravitation theory. Speculation had now reached the stage where it needed observational support, but progress was again slowed down by the need for still greater advances in observational equipment.

V

The Telescope Makers

BY THE MID-EIGHTEENTH century two basic kinds of telescope were in use—the refractor and the reflector. The reflector came in various forms, each using two mirrors—a large one to gather the light and a small one to direct the image to a convenient position for observation. In practice this meant having either a small flat mirror to direct the image to the side of the tube, as in Newton's instrument, or a small curved mirror to bring the image to the rear of the tube, as in Gregory's design (which used a concave mirror) or the method proposed by Giovanni (?) Cassegrain (which employed a convex mirror). The Gregorian type had a very small field of view, which was a nuisance astronomically speaking, although instrument makers like James Short (1710–1768) manufactured a great number, and the image they gave was so good that it offset the disadvantage of the small field. Short made a few telescopes of Newtonian design, but it was John Hadley (1682–1744) who made the majority, mounting them on a large wooden framework that was easy to use: those who favoured a smaller, less bulky instrument than the refractor chose one or the other. Cassegrain's pattern which had been theoretically torn to shreds by Newton, was little used and only came into its own in the nineteenth century after Newton's god-like image had become a little tarnished.

The refractor still suffered from two optical defects inherent in its design and caused by the lenses themselves. One was the fault of chromatic aberration, which gave annoying coloured fringes round bright objects and which had led Newton to design his reflector; the other was the inability of the ordinary kind of lens to provide an image that was sharp all over. This 'spherical aberration' was due to the spherical curves of the lenses themselves and could only be mitigated by making the curves very gentle, resulting in a long distance between the lens and its focus where the image is formed and so in telescopes of inordinate length. The large refractor belonging to the Royal Society used lenses donated by Christiaan Huygens, and it was 123 feet long, whereas a reflector of similar abilities constructed by Hadley was only 62 inches long. Yet the reflector was not as efficient as it might be, and when James Bradley (1692–1762) and James Pound (*fl.* 1700) compared the two instruments on Wanstead Common they found that the refractor gave rather brighter images. The reason lay in the construction of the mirror. Glass mirrors with a backing of mercury were tried, but they were unsuccessful and speculum metal was then the only alternative. Newton had used this alloy, manufacturing it with a combination of tin, copper, brass, and a little arsenic, but every constructor developed his own formula: sometimes this led to a vast amount of experimenting and William Molyneux, a friend of Bradley's, tried upwards of one hundred and fifty alloys before he was satisfied. The work of Short and Hadley made it seem likely that the reflector would supersede the refractor, for Newton's investigations on the dispersal of white light into its separate colours, and his theoretical arguments about dispersion through glass, were taken as conclusive proof that nothing could be done to ameliorate the drawbacks of chromatic aberration through lenses. But there were a few astonomers and opticians who were not fully convinced by Newton.

The first dissenting voice came from David Gregory (1661–1708), James Gregory's nephew and a friend and correspondent of Newton. David Gregory argued that since the human eye did not give images surrounded by coloured fringes, a refracting telescope built on similar principles should provide an answer to the chromatic problem. The eye has a lens whose power to refract light and make it form an image is very similar to glass; but between the eye's lens and its light-sensitive retina in the rear is a sac of liquid that refracts with approximately the same power as water, and Gregory's suggestion clearly pointed to a refractor with its main lens made of more than one component, although whether he was thinking of a lens made of two glass disks is doubtful: more likely he was literally thinking of a glass lens and a container of water. According to

Newton, any kind of glass would disperse colours to the same extent as it refracted the light and thus give chromatic aberration, and there is no reason to believe that Gregory thought otherwise—his suggestion was to use a different substance altogether in combination with the lens.

Gregory made his suggestion in 1695, but it was not pursued by the practical opticians, and the whole idea might have lain fallow for a very long time were it not that the notion also occurred some three decades later to Chester More Hall (fl 1733) a barrister whose hobby was experimenting in optics. Unlike Gregory, Hall was not content to make the suggestion alone, but wanted to follow it up empirically: to this end he obtained two lenses, one made of crown glass, then customary for optical work, and another of flint glass, a considerably denser material that was used almost exclusively for bottles. When he tried them in combination, the images he obtained were free from coloured fringes, but being a modest and quiet man he kept his success secret—or so he thought. However, Hall had not ground the lenses himself but had employed two professional London opticians, one to manufacture the crown component and the other the flint, and although he believed that this procedure would allow him to keep his ideas to himself, he had not allowed for the fact that opticians were in the habit of sub-contracting their orders. In this case it so happened that both employed the same craftsman, and the news of Hall's discovery spread gradually among other opticians in the City.

The first man to appreciate its significance was John Dollond (1706–1761), who had also been turning the question over in his mind after correspondence with the German mathematician Leonard Euler 1707–1783); the latter having arrived at an answer along the lines of that reached by Gregory. Euler's suggestions for a practical solution were not successful, but they stimulated Dollond to try all manner of ways of combining water-filled prisms and lenses, although without any real degree of success. Only after correspondence with Samuel Klingerstierna (c. 1690–1789), professor of mathematics at Upsala, a practical clue given by George Bass, the craftsman who had actually fashioned the lenses for Hall, and evidence in the form of a magnifying glass he saw in Bass's workshop, could Dollond set about computing and grinding crown glass and flint glass combinations. After numerous trials carried out with a great deal of perseverance, he was successful and in 1754 fashioned an excellent achromatic or colour-free refracting telescope lens. John Dollond, originally an immigrant silk-weaver, was now in partnership with his son Peter (c. 1730–1820), who had opened a small optical business a few years earlier. Peter persuaded his father to apply for a patent and soon achromatic telescopes were being manufactured and sold. All were small, since large lenses of flint glass were unobtainable, but they were extremely useful for measuring star positions; Maskelyne soon employed one at Greenwich and French astronomers were not long in taking up the new invention. After his father's death in 1761 Peter began to enforce the patent, having lawsuits with many leading opticians all of whom were happily manufacturing achromatic instruments, and he invariably won and was awarded damages. The Dollond business flourished and Peter designed even better instruments with a combination of three different lenses instead of two; these, although they corrected chromatic aberration within certain limits, could not remove it completely. Maskelyne was again in the forefront of purchasers and was so pleased with the instrument he obtained that he gave it a small room all to itself at Greenwich so that it could be used without interruption.

An astronomical telescope is useless without a firm and steady mount. The old refractors of inordinate length were usually suspended from the top of a large mast by ropes, and the eyepiece end was clamped in an adjustable wooden framework. This was a cumbersome method and hardly conducive to either easy or lengthy observing sessions, since the rotation of the Earth constantly shifted star and planetary images and it was impossible to follow them for long. With the advent of the small achromatic telescope, the possibility of making a mounting that would allow the astronomer to follow celestial bodies in their passage across the heavens became a practical proposition. The basic need was for a mount designed to permit tracking the moving star with only a simple rotation of the telescope, and this meant having the mounting tilted over so that it lay parallel to the Earth's axis: for then a simple rotation could copy the Earth's rotation and a star would remain in the centre of the field of view. Such an 'equatorial' mounting was first designed

95

and built in about 1630 by Christopher Scheiner in Germany—it was made of wood and was simple enough, but it carried a small telescope for observing the Sun, and was highly successful. Flamsteed adopted a similar kind of mount for one of his sextants which was fitted with a telescope, while the Paris Observatory used its own designs, and as the years went by private observers applied the scheme wherever practicable. With the light engineering techniques available in the eighteenth and early nineteenth centuries, the method could only be used for small telescopes. When it came to large instruments for studying the nature of the heavens rather than measuring positions, the mounting had to be so rugged that only something of the simplest kind would do, and the equatorial was out of the question. Not until the days of heavy precision engineering in the latter half of the nineteenth century was there sufficient experience to design, let alone build, the kind of mountings that have become commonplace today.

The problem facing the astronomer who wanted to study the stars and nebulae, to reach conclusions about their distribution, and follow the pioneer work of men like Halley and Wright, was to find an instrument which would make even the most far-off stars visible, and this meant being able to observe those that were very dim because of their great distance in space. Certainly the precise distance of even the nearest stars was not known in the eighteenth or early nineteenth centuries, but observations at Greenwich and elsewhere had made it clear that they were far further away than the planets—so far, in fact, that all attempts to make any measure across the gulf separating them from the Sun had failed. But if measurement failed, at least observations could provide a clue to their distribution and to their nature, provided always that really dim objects could be charted and examined, and this meant telescopes of large aperture. The front lens or object glass of a refractor and the main mirror of a reflector are used to collect the light emitted from celestial bodies and form it into an image: the larger they are, the more light they receive and the more they can render visible dim objects. Since the whole surface gathers the light, it is the area of the lens or mirror which is a guide to their 'light grasping' power: what this means in practical terms is that an increase of twice the diameter will give a light grasp four times greater, and an

William Herschel, shown holding in his hand a note about the discovery of the planet Uranus but here called 'The Georgian Planet'. Engraving by William Scriven from a crayon drawing by John Russell.

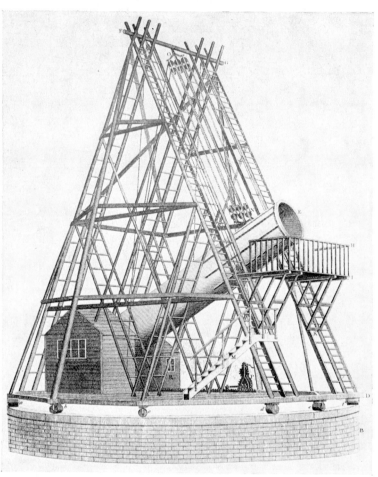

William Herschel's giant forty-foot long reflecting telescope. This engraving by J. Pass appeared in the *Encylopaedia Londinensis*, in a volume that was published *c.* 1819 and is unusual in that it shows the brick foundations on which the telescope was supported.

(*Ronan Picture Library*)

increase by a factor of three will step up the light grasp by nine times. Diameter of lens or mirror becomes a crucial matter.

However, in the eighteenth century a refractor was superior to a reflector of the same aperture because the efficiency of the speculum mirrors was so very low and, although they varied between one manufacturer and another, they never allowed as much light to reach the eye as would a lens. Also, good mirrors were hard to make. John Hadley had been the first to fashion the surface of a telescope mirror with the correct parabolic curve —earlier constructors had been content to make them with a spherical surface which was much easier to prepare but failed to produce as good an image—but the art of parabolising was only obtained after much practice and it called for a high degree of skill. And, since the speculum metal was made of expensive materials like tin, antimony and silver, good mirrors for reflecting telescopes were dear and no one manufactured the large sizes that were needed to investigate the stellar universe. Anyone wanting such a mirror had no alternative but to make his own. This was the situation when William Herschel 1738–1822) came on the scene in the 1760's.

Herschel was born in Hanover and became an oboeist in the band of the Hanoverian Foot Guards. He was a good musician but the military life was not his forte. After a brief visit to England in 1755 with the Hanoverian troops who came over when there was fear of a French invasion, and defeat at the battle of Hastenbeck a couple of years later, Herschel abandoned the Seven Years War, dismissed himself from a service in which he had never been formally enlisted, and returned to England. He took work as a musician and after a variety of appointments settled down in Nash's fashionable Bath, set up house, and was joined by his sister who acted as his housekeeper. 'The theory of music,' he later wrote in a note about his career,[1] 'being connected with mathematics had induced me very early to read in Germany all that had been written upon the subject of harmony; and when not long after my arrival in England the valuable book of Dr Smith's Harmonics came into my hands, I perceived my ignorance and had recourse to other authors for information, by which I was drawn on from one branch of mathematics to another.' Although he was a professional musician, his leisure interests turned increasingly to mathematics and, as his memoranda show, to astronomy: he observed Venus and an eclipse of the Sun, and in Bath he met Richard Robinson, Primate of Ireland and founder of the observatory at Armagh. His interest in astronomy was strengthened and after hiring telescopes, he bought lenses, and later had metal cast for making mirrors. By 1777 Herschel wrote, 'All my leisure time was given to preparing telescopes and contriving proper stands for them', and two years later,' I gave up so much of my time to astronomical preparations that I reduced the number of my scholars so as seldom to attend more than three or four per day.'[2] Obviously Urania was taking precedence over Euterpe and according to his diary for January 1782, 'I gave up much time to astronomy and also attended many scholars. Some of them made me give them astronomical instead of musical lessons.'[3]

What would have happened to Herschel's livelihood and musical career if this double life had continued one cannot guess, but fortunately his interest and his dogged perseverance paid off. On the night of Tuesday, 13 March, 1781 Herschel was engaged in one of his customary observing sessions, using a reflecting telescope about 7 feet long with a mirror of about 5 inches aperture that had cost him many nights of grinding and polishing to the correct parabolic shape. It was a fine instrument and with it he noticed a peculiar object which he could only describe as 'a curious either nebulous star or perhaps a comet', and four nights later when he observed again in the same area of the sky, he recorded:[4] 'I looked for the Comet or Nebulous Star and found that it is a Comet, for it has changed its place.' After this he followed its progress, as was necessary if enough information was to be obtained for an orbit to be computed, and in April the discovery was announced to the Royal Society. Maskelyne at Greenwich looked for the object and observations were also made by Thomas Hornsby (fl. 1770) at the observatory at Oxford. Maskelyne soon found that the object was behaving more like a planet than a comet, although Hornsby had no such qualms. On the Continent others took up the observations, and the famous cataloguer Charles Messier wrote to Herschel to enquire how he had recognised it as a moving body at all, since no apparent motion was noticeable to him during a whole night's observing. Herschel pointed out that he had noticed it was something quite different from a star, even though he could not be certain of its true nature—a fine tribute to his home-made telescope. Three continental mathematicians finally solved the problem—Jean Bochart de Sarron (1730–1794) and Simon Laplace (1749–1827) in France, and the Finn, Anders Lexell (1740–1784), working in Russia—by proving that the object had an almost circular orbit which they calculated lay about twice as far from the Sun as Saturn. Since no comet ever moves in a circular or near circular orbit (as Halley had shown), the new object must be a planet, the first to be discovered in recorded history.* Herschel wanted to call the new planet Georgium Sidus after George III, but continental astronomers (reasonably enough) did not like the name George's Star since the object was not a star and George III had nothing to do with its discovery. Their views prevailed and in accordance with tradition the new planet was named after a classical deity, Uranus.

The discovery was unique and brought Herschel's name before the learned world: it also brought his name to the attention of George III, which was far more to the point so far as his career was concerned. The king was interested in astronomy and had built and equipped Kew Observatory for his own use, and he summoned Herschel to his presence. After an audience, the 7-foot reflector with which Herschel had made his observations was set up at Greenwich and examined by Maskelyne and 'every gentleman acquainted with astronomical telescopes' for the next month, and without exception they 'declared it to exceed in distinctness and magnifying power all they had seen before'.[5] It was next taken to Windsor for the delectation of the royal family, and it was so successful there that Herschel's friends suggested he should hint that he would like to direct the Kew Observatory, the previous director, Dr Demainbray, having just died. In the event, the directorship was passed to Demainbray's son, but the king promised to make Herschel 'independent of music'. In 1782 Herschel was installed at Datchet with a salary of £200 a year, later increased to £250 so that his sister Caroline could act as his assistant, and within five years £4,000 was pro-

* The five planets, Mercury, Venus, Mars, Jupiter and Saturn are all clearly visible with the unaided eye and have been known from primitive times. Uranus is visible on occasion without a telescope, appearing as a very dim star, but generally speaking a telescope is required and for this reason it was unknown to early astronomers.

duced from the privy purse for the construction of what was to be the world's largest telescope.

This royal support marked not only a change in Herschel's career but a stride forward in British astronomy, as Herschel was now free to tackle the problems of stellar astronomy without any distractions; his duties as a Royal Astronomer—he was never Astronomer Royal—were only that he should now and again attend on the royal family to show them the heavens through a telescope, and even this duty soon lapsed. But what the royal family missed science gained, for Herschel had extraordinary powers of endurance, equalled only by those of his sister who threw up her promising musical career to devote her life to assisting her brother's investigations.

Herschel's abilities as a telescope maker were outstanding. Very sensibly he concentrated on building reflectors, since these could provide him with the large apertures and increased light grasp that he needed for stellar astronomy, and before he moved to Datchet he had already constructed a reflector with a mirror of over 19 inches diameter and a focal length of 20 feet. It is true that this was crudely mounted by a pulley-block supported from a pole in the fashion of the earlier large refractors, but he gained much experience with it, which was to be invaluable in his professional observing work. Constructing this 20-foot instrument was also good practice for his later telescope building, for he had to gain his expertise the hard way and learn from his failures: there was no one who would or could teach him the technique of mirror making and casting. His only sources of information were books like Robert Smith's *Compleat Opticks*, published as long ago as 1738, and the various scientific papers about the subject such as that written in the 1770's by John Mudge, a physician who made telescopes as a hobby and who was a brother of the famous clockmaker. Grinding and polishing the brittle metal mirrors was extremely difficult and called for refined techniques, but even worse was the business of casting the speculum metal disks themselves. Herschel used to do this in the stone-flagged kitchen of his house in Bath, and not long before his move to Datchet one such casting nearly ended in tragedy. He had decided to build an even larger mirror with a focal length of 30 feet and a diameter of 36 inches: for a reflector this was quite exceptional and the problem of casting

100

occupied most of Herschel's waking hours for weeks on end. He built a mould of loam in the approved fashion, hardening its interior by burning a load of charcoal, and poured the molten metal in, but there was a slight leak in the mould and the mirror cracked in cooling. Undaunted, Herschel repaired the mould and remelted the metal, and slightly altered its composition to make it less brittle, and everything was prepared for recasting; but at this juncture the melting oven cracked and nearly a quarter of a ton of molten metal ran over the floor, cracking the flagstones and making pieces of them fly all over the room so that the workmen had to run for their lives while Herschel, exhausted, collapsed on a pile of bricks. The idea of a 30 foot telescope was temporarily abandoned.

On moving to Datchet Herschel once more started to consider the construction of a really large instrument, and this he began to design along the lines of the 20-foot telescope, which he re-mounted on a more robust and more convenient wooden stand rather more than 20 feet high. But Datchet proved to be damp and unhealthy, and by 1786 the Herschels were installed instead in a charming house at Slough, where Caroline had a small reflecting telescope of her own. With this she discovered eight comets in the next eleven years—a record of which any professional could be proud—and she might well have done more if she had not sacrificed her own observing programme to help her brother.

The refurbished 20-foot telescope proved a fine instrument and was Herschel's favourite, yet for reasons that will become clear presently, he determined to construct something much larger and with a greatly increased light grasp. This was to have a focal length of 40 feet, a mirror with the unprecedented diameter of 48 inches, and a novel optical system by which Herschel hoped to increase even further its power to render dim objects visible. His method was to simplify the optics by doing away with a second mirror to direct the light to the side of the tube, and observe by looking directly down the front of the tube. The disadvantages of this scheme were that the main mirror had to be tilted slightly, thus producing a slight distortion of the image, and a small amount of incoming light was blotted out by the observer's head; however Herschel thought that these drawbacks would be outweighed by the gain in light he would obtain by omitting the second mirror, which always introduced losses of the order of fifty per cent. The new scheme was only practicable for a telescope with a large enough aperture to make the light loss caused by the observer of little significance.

Building the 40-foot telescope was an expensive undertaking and would have been impossible but for the financial support that George III generously provided. The labour force fluctuated between thirty and forty, depending on the processes involved, three mirrors were cast in London, one of which was useless, and much time was spent on grinding and polishing them. Herschel tried polishing by hand, using ten workmen to operate the huge shaped metal disks that were designed for the purpose, but the workmen could not agree amongst themselves 'in those delicate attentions which are required in polishing mirrors, and those indications of the state of the mirror and of the polisher which were obtained by touch when polishing by hand ... so that former experience became almost useless'.[6] There was nothing for it but to try to design a mechanical polishing machine to replace the argumentative workmen. A machine for ordinary lens manufacture was quite usual, but a device for so large a mirror was a different matter; yet he was soon ready and at last, in February 1787, the first mirror could be mounted for test. 'The apparatus for the 40-foot telescope was by this time so far completed, that I could put the mirror in to the tube and direct it to a celestial object, but having no eyeglass [eyepiece] fixed ... I went into the tube and laying down near the mouth of it I held the eyeglass in my hand and soon found the place of focus. The object I viewed was the nebula in the belt of Orion, and I found the figure of the mirror, though far from perfect, better than I had expected.'[8]

Herschel was encouraged, but it was not until two years later that the second mirror was finished, mounted, and the whole telescope ready to take part in his observing programme. As soon as he began using it Herschel discovered a new satellite of Saturn or, rather, confirmed a tentative discovery of two years earlier; but his main work with it was to try to discern the layout of the heavens and solve the problem of the nebulae. The giant 40-foot, however, was never a favourite instrument and did not quite come up to expectations: it was cumbersome to operate, the ton of heavy mirror tended to distort slightly in certain positions, the atmosphere of Slough was not ideal for so large an instrument, and it gradually fell more and more into disuse until after a couple of years of intermittent work, it became no more than a curiosity. All the same it attracted a good deal of attention. The famous Italian astronomer Giuseppe Piazzi (1746–1826), discoverer of the first of the planetoids—those small planetary fragments that orbit the Sun mainly between the orbits of Mars and Jupiter—came to see the giant of Slough, and the well-known French astronomer Joseph Lalande (1732–1807) made two visits—possibly as much because of Caroline as the 40-foot; there was a deputation from the Paris Observatory, and any royalty or nobility at Windsor seemed to count a visit part of their expected entertainment. Most visitors came and went without incident, although Piazzi hurt himself falling over a protruding metal bar in the dark, but during their own observing sessions both Herschel and Caroline had accidents; Herschel fell at least once from a temporary observing platform he had rigged up, while Caroline once suffered more serious injury when in the snow she fell on a large metal hook from one of the rope supports of the telescope; typical of her, she made no cry lest she should disturb her brother's work.

Herschel's work in stellar astronomy was notable because of the immense size and superior quality of his telescopes and his almost superhuman perseverance for more than thirty years. He seems to have been one of those men who need but little sleep, and something of his immense observing programme can be gauged from the fact that he made in all four complete and detailed surveys of the northern skies, undertook careful star counts in no less than 3,400 selected areas of the sky and catalogued upwards of 2,500 nebulae and similar objects as well as making a vast series of measurements on double and variable stars. Yet even this is not the sum of his achievements. He built something like 400 mirrors of various sizes and sold at least 69 complete instruments which were bought by amateurs and professionals and by continental royalty; he experimented on solar radiation; and he found time to collate and analyse his observations and produce a string of more than 70 scientific papers, ranging from straightforward descriptions of what he had seen to speculations about the construction of the entire universe. The quantity of his scientific work would in itself have more than satisfied the most prolific of his contemporaries, and luckily its volume did no damage to its quality—this was always high, and on occasions outstanding.

When he began his stellar work Herschel hoped to solve a problem that had taxed the ingenuity of astronomers since the Renaissance: the problem of measuring the distance of the stars. The general thesis then, as now, was to utilise the Earth's orbital motion to show up an apparent shift (parallax) between the nearer stars and those that are more distant. Observations made when the Earth is in one position, and then repeated six months later when the Earth is on the other side of its orbit, would, it was thought, provide two views of the heavens seen from observing positions separated by some 180,000,000 miles (the diameter of the Earth's orbit). This would give an apparent shift of the nearer stars against the background of those too distant to show any change at all, so that, by measuring the shift and knowing the diameter of the Earth's orbit, the distance of the nearer stars could be calculated. The method is analagous to the kind of observation one makes from a moving car, where with every shift in position of the car as it moves along the road, the nearby trees or lamp standards themselves appear to move with respect to the more distant background of buildings or countryside. Herschel well knew that previous attacks on the problem had drawn a blank because the shift appeared too small to detect, and it occurred to him that he might obtain the required accuracy by using a powerful telescope and carefully measuring the shift of pairs of stars that fortuitously appeared close to one another in the sky: his hope being that in these cases one star—the nearer—would show a shift with respect to the other, its more distant companion. Using a micrometer with two 'wires' made of silkworm thread fitted on to his eyepiece, his practice was to place it so that one thread lay over one of the stars, and adjust the position of the second thread until it lay across the other star: a carefully cut screw and engraved disk gave a precise measure of the separation between the threads and therefore between the stars. This was not a perfect system and he later replaced the threads by a device that gave two bright spots of light to coincide with the pair of stars, and produced greater accuracy. The measurements Herschel made began to give him encouragement, but, as time went by, he found that the small shifts he measured did not become greater and then decrease again as was to be expected if they were due to parallax; they followed some quite independent law of behaviour. Further observations made it clear that what he had been observing were 'binary' star systems, i.e. those in which the two stars orbit around each other: those where he had detected a shift of position all showed a 'periodical revolution', and after analysis the observations demonstrated that the attraction of each star for the other was gravitational, proving conclusively that Newtonian theory operated in the vast depths of space. The observations were unsuccessful in determining parallax and it was not until after Herschel's death that reasonable measurements of stellar distance were to be made.

By the time Herschel was at work, Halley's discovery of the proper motions of stars was well accepted and it was generally agreed that all stars must possess a motion of this kind. Herschel not only gave additional confirmation, but also made an analysis of his results to try to discover the motion of the Sun in space; for, since the Sun is a star, it should have a proper motion of its own. Yet this is another of those problems that it is easier to state than to solve, for since the Earth's orbit will take part in any motion that the Sun may have, the only way to detect such motion is to watch for a growing displacement in star positions of a specific kind. Herschel was not the only astronomer to consider the matter—Tobias Mayer (1732–1762), Lalande, and a Scots astronomer, Alexander Wilson (1766–1813), had all discussed the question—but he was the first to reach a practical result. The kind of motion that Herschel sought was similar to that which may be observed in a fleet of ships all out of sight of land. Consider all the fleet stationary except one ship whose course takes it into the middle of the others. As the moving ship continues its approach to the fleet, coming ever closer to them, each of the stationary ships will appear to move to one side or the other. If the moving ship sails through them, the fleet will be seen spread out to the left and the right, and then, if the moving ship continues its course, the fleet will appear to close up behind it. This effect of perspective can also be seen from a moving car, the road ahead seeming to spread out, pass by the sides of the car, and then close in behind it. Herschel therefore had to seek stars that seemed to behave in just this kind of way, moving away to the left or to the right from a particular place in the heavens; but the observations were complex, since all the stars must be assumed to possess motions of their own as well.

To begin with he hoped to extract the evidence from double stars, believing he might notice a change in their relative positions that could only be accounted for by such a motion. He carefully selected 350 doubles spread in different directions through space; but his later work, showing that many were binary systems, vitiated any hope of a result from observations of this kind. Meanwhile Herschel had a second string to his bow, for Maskelyne and Lalande had tabulated the proper motions of thirteen stars, and after he had analysed these he announced that the Sun appeared to be moving towards a point in space in the constellation of Hercules. Later, when Maskelyne published proper motions for thirty-six of the brighter stars Herschel recalculated his result: again he found that the Sun appeared to be moving towards Hercules, but now he assigned it a slightly different direction. Later still, in 1806, he again returned to the question, since he also wanted to determine the speed as well as the direction of the Sun's motion; but this was something of a failure since he had insufficient information to allow him to compute the Sun's velocity in miles per second or any other specific units. All the same one result that came out of all this work—besides a pretty correct idea of which way the Sun moved—was the fact that the proper motions of Maskelyne's three dozen stars did not seem to be distributed at random, as Herschel and others had expected, but gave evidence of showing a preference for moving in the same direction as the Sun. This was no spurious effect, and later research using the proper motions of hundreds rather than dozens of stars has shown that it is due to the movement of stars as a whole as they orbit round the centre of the galaxy. But Herschel could not appreciate that the observations were likely to lead to such a result.

Another task that Herschel undertook was the cataloguing of the brightnesses or 'magnitudes' of stars. The results were useful to later observers, forming the raw material from which they could build their own analyses, but to Herschel, with his star counts all over the sky, they formed the basis of the research he made into what he called the 'construction of the heavens'. This was a valiant attempt to discover the distribution and pattern of the stars in space, rather along the lines of Thomas Wright (although Herschel knew nothing of Wright's hypothesis). The basic problem was to decide about the distances of the stars, and this was not easy since the only star whose distance was known with anything more than a guess was the Sun. What should Herschel do? Assume such distribution as seemed to him aesthetically desirable, or work out the positions of the stars on some suitable physical basis? We might expect the aesthetic approach to appeal more strongly to a mathematician and musician. But no: Herschel quite rightly decided to make some scientific estimate of stellar distances. Clearly some assumptions had to be made, and he decided to take it that the stars were evenly distributed throughout space and that all were of the same brightness—the apparent differences as one sees them in the sky being due solely to their different distances. On this hypothesis the Sun appears brightest because it is the nearest of all the stars, and the very dim ones that we can hardly discern are the most distant. Herschel knew that the assumption was not precisely correct—or at least was unlikely to be—but he argued that men, or oak trees, taken by and large are approximately the same size, and that his assumption was valid: a view that he doggedly held to in spite of flaws in the hypothesis pointed out by the cleric, John Michell (1724–1793). But the details need not concern us; here it is only Herschel's broad and brilliant sketch of the stellar system that matters.

The conclusion Herschel reached was similar in many ways to Wright's, although he did not consider the Milky Way as extending indefinitely in the form of a flat disk: to Herschel the stellar system was confined within a shape not unlike a flat rectangular box that was split open at one end. For an observer, like ourselves, within the box and not far from the centre, most of the stars would seem to spread in a luminous band across the sky, just like the Milky Way; the comparatively few stars lying over the 'sides' of the box we should see covering the more sparsely populated areas of the sky, forming the constellations with which the astronomer is familiar. But Herschel did not fall into the error of thinking that everything in the heavens is permanent: indeed he suggested that stars gravitate towards one another and make clusters, and that great concourses of stars like those forming the Milky Way would always break up into smaller units. This disintegrating universe was fed by nebulae which as time passed condensed into stars that would then form small clusters, and every stage was visible to the observer.

Herschel appreciated the surprising fact that since light takes time to travel, we see the universe in various stages of development. If we observe close to, the light has only recently set out on its journey, and we observe things very nearly as they are: but if we are penetrating deep into the further reaches of space with a telescope, then the light will have set out long ago and we observe the universe as it was in past ages. Since he had no definite figures for stellar distances, Herschel was unable to say how long ago, but at least 'we can, as it were, extend the range of our experience to an immense duration'.[7] Using the simile of a garden, he argued, 'is it not almost the same thing, whether we live successively to witness the germination, blooming, foliage, fecundity, fading, withering, and corruption of a plant, or whether a vast number of specimens, selected from every stage through which the plant passes in the course of its existence, be brought at once to our view?' Not content to stop here, Herschel went on to consider the beginning of his evolutionary universe, but he was less successful in this and the best he could do was to conclude that the break-up of the Milky Way 'is a kind of chronometer that may be used to measure the time of its past and future existences; and although we do not know the rate of going of this mysterious chronometer, it is nevertheless certain, that since the breaking up of the parts of the milky way affords a proof that it cannot last for ever, it equally bears witness that its past duration cannot be admitted to be infinite'.[8]

Not all Herschel's ideas were as sound as those on the construction of the heavens. He suggested that the Sun might be inhabited for, although it was obviously extremely hot, the heat could, Herschel thought, be confined to an outer atmosphere; and his attempts to discuss the optics of 'Newton's rings' (coloured rings observed when two pieces of glass are placed close to one another) were wildly in error, partly because of his conservatism over ideas about the nature of light itself. But his adventures into the field of physics did lead to one useful result —the discovery of radiant heat from the Sun. He was led to this

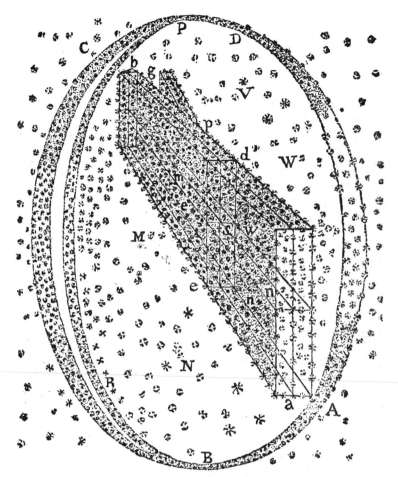

William Herschel's scheme of the Milky Way and the stars composing it. The areas of sky A, B, C, D and R are those which lie in the Milky Way and which he had observed: the areas M, N, V and W are other areas of the sky also observed by Herschel. They appear, as all star observations do, to be made on a sphere and are thus depicted here, but Herschel concluded that the Milky Way was really shaped like a long box. The stars in the box are indicated by small letters which, in general, refer to those parts of the 'box' which, when observed, appeared to give stars on the sphere at the points marked by the capital letters. The observed 'split' of the Milky Way at CP is due to a 'split' in the box at bg. The observer is taken to be at s, the position of the Sun. This engraving appeared in a volume of the *Encyclopaedia Londinensis* that was published about 1807.

(*Ronan Picture Library*)

by analysing the heating effects of the different colours of sunlight dispersed by a prism, and his experiments proved beyond all doubt that as well as sending out light the Sun radiates invisible heat rays that behave in a similar way to light rays, except that they cannot be seen and can only be detected with a thermometer. The heat rays, which lie below the red end of the spectrum produced by the prism, subsequently became known as 'infra red' radiation. Later, Herschel's discovery was to assume more importance when coupled with the discovery of the German physicist, Johann Ritter, that other invisible solar rays lie beyond the violet end of the spectrum—so-called ultra-violet radiation.

The importance of another side of Herschel's work was recognised very quickly—just after he had made his observations, in fact—and this was the study of the nebulae. Halley had already considered them and found they shone with their own 'lustre', but with his larger telescopes Herschel was able to study them more closely. Some patches that appeared hazy in smaller telescopes he found he could separate into stars; but others, do what he would to resolve them into stars by increasing the magnifying power of his instrument, remained hazy and ill-defined shapes. 'Other objects there are, where a great space-gathering power will only increase the brightness of the nebulosity,' he wrote in 1814,[9] and went on to comment, 'But when an object is of such a construction, or at such a distance from us, that the highest power of presentation, which hitherto has been applied to it, leaves it undertermined whether it belong to the class of nebulae or of stars, it may then be called ambiguous.' Originally, Herschel had believed that with a really large telescope he would be able to resolve all nebulae into separate stars, but a lifetime of observing made him revise his opinion, especially since he discovered a number of stars that seemed to be situated right in the midst of 'a shining fluid, of nature totally unknown to us'. These 'planetary nebulae' as Herschel called them, because through a telescope their bright disks at first glance looked like the disk of a planet, led him to consider the possibility that two kinds of nebula existed in space, and so other astronomers became interested in the problem.

The nebulae raised all kinds of questions. Were the 'lucid' ones made of a shining 'fluid' that condensed into stars, and

110

were the star clusters truly the results of stars collecting together under the influence of gravitation? Alexander Wilson certainly supported the latter contention and there were others who felt the same way: but was Herschel correct in going a step further and claiming that our own Milky Way was a system on its own, condensed out of an original background of stars, and but one of a wider and more extensive universe composed of hundreds, perhaps thousands, of other such separate condensations? Could we surmise that nebulae were for the most part clusters of stars, so that some of the hazy patches that Herschel's telescope picked out would indeed appear as systems showing separate stars in an even larger telescope than the 40-foot?

The man who tackled the problem was William Parsons, later third Earl of Rosse (1800–1867). Many British astronomers thought him misguided, since they believed that after Herschel's 40-foot nothing larger could be constructed, that the reflector had had its day, and that it would soon be replaced by the achromatic refractor now that larger glass lenses could be made. There was some substance in their argument, as will become evident in Chapter VII when we consider the quest for precision in astronomical measurement, but Rosse pinned his faith on constructing something with a light grasp far in excess of anything Herschel had built. To begin with he made smaller instruments so that he could gain the experience necessary before embarking on a giant reflector, and one of 15 inches aperture was soon followed, in 1840, by another with a mirror 36 inches in diameter. This performed extremely well, and showed double stars with a clear black patch of sky between them, thus making it obvious that he was using the right techniques. Rosse borrowed many of his ideas from Herschel—at least from those few facts on telescope making that Herschel had published—and to begin with even mounted his 36-inch in a similar way to Herschel's 20-foot and 40-foot instruments. But for his chief enterprise, the construction of a reflector with a mirror nothing less than 72 inches in diameter, he had to think for himself, as nothing on such a scale had been built before. He was nevertheless encouraged by his 36-inch because, as far as he could tell, it was 'the most powerful telescope that has ever been constructed', exceeding Herschel's 40-foot long 48-inch aperture monster because of the higher reflecting power and superior shape of

111

the mirror, and in the 1840's he set about planning and putting his massive scheme into operation.

The heart of the instrument was the mirror and on this Rosse lavished every care, bringing to bear his fortune, his engineering abilities, and his knowledge of foundry techniques. He designed and had constructed a giant grinding and polishing machine driven by a steam engine, while he also built a special mould for casting that would quickly and evenly disperse the heat of the molten speculum metal. He wasted no time in getting his project off the ground and in the middle of April 1842, the first casting took place. For two hours the crucible was heated and for a further ten hours the metal had been heated and melted. At last, in the evening, the metal was poured into the mould. Rosse's assistant Thomas Romney Robinson (1792–1882) has left a fine description of the operation, which was carried out in the grounds of Rosse's home, Birr Castle. 'Above, the sky crowded with stars and illuminated with a most brilliant moon, seemed to look down auspiciously on their work. Below, the furnaces poured out huge columns of nearly monochromatic yellow flame, and the ignited crucibles during their passage through the air were fountains of red light, producing on the towers of the castle and the foliage of the trees, such accidents of colour as might almost transport fancy to the planets of a contrasted double star.'[10] Although the mould quickly cooled from the bottom upwards, the top of the mirror was still red-hot when it was carried on a simple railway to a large oven, where the final cooling was controlled so that the temperature only dropped little by little: sixteen weeks later the mirror was ready for polishing and grinding. Rosse was a patient man, but even his patience must have been stretched nearly to the limit when the mirror was accidentally broken and the casting had to be done again. This time Rosse increased the amount of copper used so as to make the mirror less brittle, but the casting was full of pits and, although these were ground away, he decided to make yet another. More disasters followed, but at last a fifth mirror turned out perfectly and it was ground, polished and mounted within a month.

The telescope was so large that it was beyond even Rosse's engineering abilities to devise a practical mounting that would permit the instrument to point towards any object in the sky,

William Parsons, third Earl of Rosse, who spent much of his private fortune on building a telescope far larger than Herschel's in the hope of determining the nature of the nebulae, From a woodcut made in 1867.

(*Ronan Picture Library*)

Rosse's giant reflector mounted between its brick walls and situated on his estate at Birr in Eire.

(Ronan Picture Library)

and in the event it had to be confined between two walls, each almost sixty feet high. The walls ran due north and south, and between them the telescope was free to swing up and down: it could therefore be pointed in a northerly or southerly direction, but the observer had to wait for the Earth's rotation to carry the stars round into the field of view. By February 1845 everything was ready and Rosse, Robinson and James South (1785–1867), an English astronomer, tried out the monster, hoping to see the nebula in Orion which Herschel had never been able to resolve completely into stars. But the sky clouded over before the nebula came into view, and they had to possess their souls in patience until another night. When they did see it, however, they too found that it could not be resolved. Yet this was no sure indication that an even larger telescope would obtain the same result; and Rosse and Robinson turned their attention to other nebulae which the new telescope revealed in plenty. They were able to pick out stars in many of these objects, and noticed that there were some nebulae that displayed a very marked spiral structure, appearing for all the world like huge celestial catherine wheels.

The 'Leviathan of Parsonstown', as it came to be known, cost some £12,000 to build, yet apart from its discovery of the spiral nature of some nebulae—the significance of which was to remain unrealised for a very long time—and its resolution of many others into stars, the instrument achieved little. This was due partly to the mounting which prevented an observer from setting his telescope on any particular star or nebula except for a few moments, and partly to the poor visibility at Parsonstown where the sky was cloudy more often than not. 'From the interruption by clouds, the slowness of finding with and managing a large instrument ... and the desire of looking well at an object when we had got it, we did not look at many objects', was what the Astronomer Royal George Airy (1801–1892) had to say;[11] nevertheless he had nothing but praise for the views of celestial bodies obtained once they were in the right position and the clouds were absent. As far as Rosse and Robinson were concerned, they disagreed with Herschel and concluded that 'no REAL nebula seemed to exist',[12] believing they were all clusters of stars. It is only fair to say that in this view they were supported by the American astronomer, William Bond (1789–1859) working at Harvard with a beautiful 15-inch diameter refractor;

H

and mere telescopic observations, be the instrument as large as desired, could never unequivocally solve the problem of the nebulae. A completely new technique was needed and this, as we shall see in Chapter VII, only arrived after the Parsonstown 72-inch had been in use for some years and both Rosse and Robinson had published their results.

But if Rosse himself made few discoveries, his telescope was used by a succession of astronomers, including his son, who proceeded to add little by little to the important task of collecting observations which could later be used by others with a more theoretical turn of mind. And, as one would expect, he was not alone in constructing large mirrors: among others accepting the challenge were James Nasmyth (1808–1890) and William Lassell (1799–1880). Both advanced telescope construction and made observations which were useful to later generations, although neither was to challenge Rosse when it came to matters of size.

Nasmyth was an engineer and is best known for his invention of the steam hammer, which led to a revolution in engineering workshop practice; but his father had early awakened in him an interest in astronomy, so that well before Rosse had built his largest instrument Nasmyth decided to enter the telescope building field himself. In his Manchester factory he had every foundry facility he could wish for and he began conservatively enough with a small telescope; but such was his enthusiasm for the glorious views of the heavens he obtained that from his garden beside the Bridgewater Canal he used sometimes to observe in his nightshirt when the weather was hot and the skies favourable, undismayed by the fact that a bargee swore he had seen a ghost moving among the trees with a coffin in its hands! But Nasmyth's greatest effort was his 20-inch mirror, which he mounted with all the engineering aplomb he could muster. Constructed of iron and on a mounting not very different from that used for a small cannon, the mirror was adapted from the design originally proposed by Cassegrain, but modified by the use of a third mirror to bring the light through one of the hollow pivots; so that Nasmyth could sit comfortably on a seat fixed to the mounting and direct the telescope where he wanted with no more effort than that required to turn a couple of handwheels. When he retired in 1856 he moved to

Penshurst in Kent and gave much of his time to astronomy, using his conveniently arranged 20-inch to the full, studying the Sun, the precise nature of sunspots and, above all, the Moon. Nasmyth's lunar studies have gone down in history, for he was a staunch supporter of the view—still today a matter of contention—that the craters and other lunar features were formed by volcanic activity. With James Carpenter (1840–1899), at one time a member of the Greenwich staff, in 1874 he produced a book, *The Moon*, in which he set out his theory and illustrated it with photographs of the most beautifully and precisely made models of sections of the lunar surface.

Lassell knew Nasmyth and said of his 20-inch mirror that it was so perfect 'it made his mouth water',[12] and it seems that while Lassell continued to make his own mirrors, ending up with a beautiful speculum of 48 inches diameter, it was to Nasmyth that he turned for the engineering of the mountings he designed. Lassell, originally a brewer, spent his leisure time observing, and when he retired he spent a number of years in Malta where he hoped for, and found, better skies. During 1859 and 1860, at his home in Liverpool, he constructed his 48-inch reflector, which had a metal equatorial mounting allowing him to follow the motion of the stars by a single movement of the telescope. But obversing with it was not as convenient as with Nasmyth's 20-inch, for the length of the telescope tube was almost 37 feet—nearly as long as Herschel's of the same aperture—and Lassell had to perch himself in a wooden tower that enabled him to reach the top of the tube, and could be carried round the telescope as the tube moved. Lassell claimed it was very convenient, but here his enthusiasm seems to have run away with him, even though the work he did with the telescope was of high quality. Unlike previous owners of large telescopes, Lassell spent a great deal of his time on the solar system, hunting for additional satellites to Saturn, Uranus and Neptune (discovered in 1846): in one of these efforts he was successful and his work proved the value of a large instrument, even in planetary work. It also emphasised the lesson, taken to heart by later astronomers, that a site with good observing conditions is vital if a large telescope is to justify the cost and effort involved in building it.

With Lassell's 48-inch reflector we come to the last days of the speculum metal mirror. In 1856, the mathematician Karl von Steinheil (1801–1870) in Munich, and the French physicist, Léon Foucault (1819–1868), independently applied a process developed by the great chemist Justus von Liebig (1803–1873) for depositing a thin even film of silver on glass, and they constructed silver-on-glass mirrors for astronomical telescopes. The silver-on-glass mirror was lighter than its speculum metal counterpart, and so easier to mount. But even more important was its efficiency, since, when freshly applied, the silvered surface reflected half as much light again as even the best speculum metal. A long and heroic chapter of telescope making was closed and a new era opened, which in the twentieth century was to increase space penetrating power to an unprecedented extent.

VI

The Neptune Scandal

ONE OF THE MOST unhappy and unfortunate incidents in the whole of British astronomy was that connected with the discovery of the planet Neptune in the mid-nineteenth century. Now, more than a century after the event, we can look back on the whole sorry story with complete impartiality and no little compassion, but at the time—1846—feelings ran high and for a while there was the danger of a permanent breach between British astronomers and their continental colleagues. The situation arose because two great minds wrestled with what lesser men considered an insoluble problem—that of discovering some explanation of the anomalous behaviour of the planet Uranus and of proving beyond any shadow of doubt that their explanation was correct.

William Herschel had discovered Uranus in 1781. It was a completely unexpected discovery since no one had even so much as suspected that any planet lay in an orbit beyond that of Saturn, and it was due to Herschel's meticulous care as an observer and the superior quality of his home-made telescopes. Once the discovery had been made, the observational astronomer rather dropped out of the picture: Herschel continued to watch his 'Georgian Star' and found two satellites orbiting round it, and William Lassell discovered two others, but it was the mathematical astronomer who began to take a more than passing interest. Those in the national observatories at Greenwich, Paris, and Berlin were busy noting the planet's position, just as they were recording the positions of the rest of the planets, but after the initial curiosity of looking at the newly discovered object their work became routine. To the mathematician, however, matters were not so dull, for Uranus unexpectedly fitted in with a peculiar relationship between the planets that had originally been discovered by Johann Daniel Titius (?–1796) and announced by him in 1772 when he published a German translation of a French treatise on natural science. Buried in the translation, the relationship might have been lost in a welter of pages unlikely to be of interest to the astronomer, had not Johann Bode (1747–1826), another German, happened upon it and republished it in his own introduction to astronomy.

The relationship was merely a series of numbers that began with 4, and then increased step by step without limit, each successive number being computed according to a simple rule,* but its interest lay in the fact that the numbers coincided very closely with the distances of the planets from the Sun. For instance, if the observed distance Earth to Sun is taken as 10, then the distances of Mercury and Venus work out as 3.8 and 7.2; and if the distance of the Earth is taken to be 10 (on Bode's law, as it has come to be called), then the law gives 4 to Mercury and 7 for Venus—both close enough to the mark—and there is a similar correspondence for Mars, Jupiter and Saturn. Perhaps the law was no more than a curiosity, a glimpse of some fictitious celestial harmony similar to the relationship between the speeds of planets in their orbits and the diatonic musical scale about which Kepler had been so enthusiastic a century before. Or so it seemed until Herschel's discovery of Uranus. Then the fact that Uranus fitted with Bode's law became too much of a coincidence and the astronomical world began to pay more attention to it, and particularly to the fact that the law gave a value for a planetary orbit between Mars and Jupiter that seemed to be unoccupied by any orbiting body at all. On the Continent a band of German astronomers organized themselves to hunt for the mysterious missing planet; but they were anticipated by Piazzi who, quite by chance, found an object whose orbit coincided with that 'predicted' by Bode's law. There was some argument about whether Piazzi's discovery, made in 1801, was in fact a planet—the philosopher Hegel had just published a 'philosophical discourse' proving by unassailable logic that seven was the maximum number of the planets—and it was only subsequent discovery of other 'asteroids', as Herschel called the

---

* The relationship, beginning with 4, is expressed simply as $4 + 3(2^n)$ giving a series of numbers 4, 7, 10, 16, 28, 52, 100, etc.

planetary fragments, most of which orbit the Sun between Mars and Jupiter, that put the final seal of respectability on Bode's numerical fantasy and was later of considerable use to the hunters of Neptune.

The mathematicians' interest in Uranus was engaged because the positional astronomers at the national observatories found that the calculated positions for the planet did not agree with their measurements. The disparity was not excessive but it did amount to what was considered an unacceptable amount, and there was a widespread desire to find some suitable explanation. A hunt through records of observations made long before the actual discovery by Herschel showed that the planet had been observed quite often although no one, including the punctilious Flamsteed, had recognised it for what it was; to these earlier observers it had merely been another star that required cataloguing along with a host of others. Yet even though these older observations were used and allowance made for the slight errors in position that they, as well as any other observations, were likely to contain, there was still something wrong. Every time previous observations were used as a basis for computing a new orbit for the planet, the calculated future positions failed to square with the observed positions as these became available. Eventually the disagreement brought into doubt the validity of Newton's gravitational theory or, to be more precise, the validity of the inverse square law. No one now doubted that universal gravitation was a fact, but it was the precise nature of the force that was called to question. Perhaps the law did not operate out further than Saturn in the way Newton had supposed—possibly the square of the distance became the cube of the distance so far away from the Sun, or conceivably the relationship was not quite so simple and direct.

There was another possible explanation that did no violence to gravitational law but rather would support it down to the last iota, and that was to consider the misbehaviour of Uranus as a result of perturbations caused by the attractions of still further planets. The idea was not new—Halley had computed the perturbing force of Jupiter on the comet of 1682—and the theory of gravitation made it possible to consider more than one disturbing force; but in practice the calculations were long and tedious. The Moon, which was subject to the gravitational pulls of both Sun and Earth, was perhaps the most obvious case, for here the equatorial bulge of the Earth and other factors complicated the issue to such a degree that new corrections were continually being found and added as extra items to the mathematical equations expressing its motion. The technique might be tedious but it worked, and the effects of Jupiter on Saturn and Saturn on Jupiter were taken care of by adding on perturbation terms to the equations that satisfied their orbits. The mathematics involved had remained the province of continental astronomers and mathematicians, since it was they who developed the calculus and could apply it to the solution of these problems.

In one sense, the complacency of mathematicians in Britain became a scandal at least in the minds of one or two young and progressive men, and in the second decade of the nineteenth century they decided to take some action. The three leaders of the new movement were Charles Babbage (1792–1871), George Peacock (1790–1858) and John Herschel (1792–1871). All three were Cambridge men, all became lifelong friends, and each had an unusual flair for mathematics. Babbage is now remembered mainly for his ingenious calculating machine, which not only performed the more usual and tedious processes of arithmetic but was capable of compiling simple mathematical tables and printing the results; but in his own day he was better known for his part in the formation of the British Association for the Advancement of Science, designed to act as a public forum for scientific matters—a job that it still carries out today. Peacock was rather more academically minded than Babbage and became both a professor of mathematics and a cleric of note; while John Herschel, the only child of William Herschel, was mathematically the most brilliant of the trio. For a time he toyed with the idea of becoming a lawyer, but in the end he chose to follow in his father's footsteps: he helped materially in the advance of stellar astronomy and gained a reputation that amounted to almost Newtonian proportions. Contemporaries at Cambridge at the end of the first decade of the nineteenth century, the three young men decided that the advance of British mathematics had been held back too long by tradition: they proposed the adoption of the obviously superior continental methods for the calculus, and started up the Analytical Society, whose avowed intent was to expunge the use of

Newton's mathematical notation. This was no wild undergraduate protest movement, but one that argued its points and published the techniques it advocated so that others could judge the case; finally it achieved some measure of success, for although it did not manage to eradicate Newton's notation the more explicit continental methods did come into use in Britain and there is no doubt that this had its due effect when in the late 1820's the problem of Uranus's perturbations had reached the most alarming proportions.

In 1821 Alexis Bouvard, a member of the staff of the Paris Observatory, published a set of tables of the motions of Uranus, calculated as precisely as possible from contemporary observations and taking into account the perturbations caused by Jupiter and Saturn. Bouvard had to neglect the early pre-discovery observations that had come to light, since they could not be compensated with any orbit obtained from up-to-date sightings. This meant rejecting Flamsteed and even Lemonnier (1715–1799), who had observed the planet on four consecutive nights and would surely have discovered it were it not for the fact that his observational results were muddled, with some of them written on a paper bag used for wig powder. Their observations, Bouvard concluded, must have contained gross errors unless some extraneous and quite unknown influence was acting on the planet—a view which does not seem to have appealed to him greatly.

Within eleven years of the publication of Bouvard's tables, the errors between his predicted positions and the observed positions were increasing 'with fearful rapidity' as the Astronomer Royal, George Airy, reported to the British Association. Since Bouvard had taken into account all known perturbations, only two answers seemed to Airy to be likely: either the Newtonian theory was to be thrown out of the window, or one had to assume that some errors existed in the tables themselves. Airy was not inclined to discard universal gravitation (which had come unscathed through a perturbation problem a couple of years before), and so he had to plump for the latter, but in doing so he ignored a third and to some astronomers more likely explanation. This was the suggestion that the discrepanices were due to the existence of an unknown planet circling the Sun in an orbit that lay still further away than Uranus's (see pages 98–99): but Airy seems to have rejected this from the start since he believed that if such a body did exist, and if it were the cause of the errors between observed and calculated values, then, as he put it to the British Association, 'it will be nearly impossible to find out its place'.[1] The problem of working out the position of a body of undetermined size travelling in an unknown orbit with only the observational discrepancies to go on was certainly a hideously difficult task—computing the perturbations of one known body caused by other known bodies all following well determined orbits was bad enough, but to do the whole operation backwards was just too much to ask, or so Airy believed. This was in many ways a strange attitude to take, especially for a man like Airy whose own mathematical abilities were considerable: clearly he knew more than enough to appreciate the enormity of the problem, but to be so emphatic seems to show a serious lack of imagination. At any rate, Airy, past pupil of George Peacock at Cambridge, Senior Wrangler, for seven years Plumian professor of astronomy and director of the university observatory, and from 1835 Astronomer Royal, had made up his mind: nothing but an intellectual earthquake would move him.

Many others shared Airy's opinion, and it needed a fresh enthusiasm, allied to a prodigious mathematical insight, to do anything in the way of proving that the diabolically difficult problem could be solved in a way specific enough to provide observers with details of where to look for the unknown planet. It also required a great deal of persuasion to prod an observatory into taking action which at worst might be a wild goose chase and at best would occupy hundreds of valuable hours of observing time. Yet there were two young men who had the necessary talents and sufficient perseverance to carry the project through: in Britain, John Couch Adams (1819–1892), and in France, Urbain Jean Joseph Leverrier (1811–1877).

Adams was a shy young Cornishman who early showed an outstanding talent for mathematics. At the age of ten he stretched the mathematical abilities of his local schoolmaster almost to breaking point, and then had to forage on his own, as his next school concentrated on classics to the exclusion of everything else: fortunately the local Mechanics' Institute had a good library where he could devour books on Newton's fluxions and read encyclopaedia articles about astronomy, and he attended the many lecture courses that the Institute held. Adams's mathematical prowess, even at the age of eighteen, is shown by diary entries that make it clear that he was then quite able to solve problems that Newton had tackled, but by methods of his own, and in 1839 he won a scholarship to Cambridge. He was now twenty and in spite of running away with every mathematical prize, he seems to have been a popular young man, even if his parents' slender finances did not allow him to live at all extravagantly. In 1841 he read Airy's dry report to the British Association and, as he wrote a week later,[2] 'Formed a design, in the beginning of this week, of investigating, as soon as possible after taking my degree, the irregularities in the motion of Uranus which are yet unaccounted for; in order to find whether they may be attributed to the action of an undiscovered planet beyond it; and if possible thence to determine the elements of its orbit etc., approximately, which would probably lead to its discovery.' Adams may have been modest and retiring but there can be no doubt of his independence of mind even in the face of a pronouncement from an Astronomer Royal. He also had considerable patience, for his finals were not held until two years later, and even then his wish to take private pupils, so as to pay something back to his family for his time at Cambridge, meant that vacations were the only time that he could really devote to his own research.

In view of what was to happen later, it is necessary to stress the outstanding nature of Adams's mathematical talents, and without going into technicalities it is worth noting that in the final tripos examinations his marks totalled 4,000 compared with 2,000 for the runner-up, Bashforth, who was by no means a poor mathematician and was later appointed to a chair of mathematics; in fact there was a greater difference between Adams and Bashforth than between Bashforth and the candidate with the lowest marks. Moreover Adams's abilities were well recognised at the university, and when he had solved the Uranus problem within twelve months and wanted new and more up-to-date observations so that he could provide a second and increasingly reliable position for the unknown planet, James Challis, the professor of astronomy, was only too ready to obtain them for him from Airy. Uranus was not the only matter occupying Adams's thoughts, however, and when a comet appeared in 1844 he deduced its orbit from observations made by Challis, who advised him to publish his results by writing a letter to the London *Times*. The next year, when Adams could move properly have benefited from similar advice, he did not receive it—indeed Challis's apathy over the discovery of the unknown disturber of Uranus's peace is one of the more peculiar and surprising aspects of the whole affair.

Progress on calculating the position of the 'undiscovered planet' continued, and by September 1845, eighteen months after he had taken his degree, Adams had reached a full solution. By assuming that the orbit of the hypothetical planet lay at the next step in distance given by Bode's law, Adams had cracked the hard nut of inverse perturbations and provided figures that gave details of the orbit and the size (mass) of the planet. It was an unprecedented mathematical exercise and appears to have been a little beyond Challis: instead of starting at once to look for the planet which he could have found from the calculations that Adams had made, he seems to have regarded the whole thing purely as a clever mathematical feat, and suggested that Adams should communicate his results not to *The Times*, but to Airy. With an introduction from Challis, Adams visited Greenwich in late September on his way to Cornwall, but Airy was away in France. Adams left a note of his results and went on vacation, but when he returned to Cambridge again he called at Greenwich. Airy was again out so Adams left his card, saying he would return later, and then called back after about an hour. He was told Airy was at dinner and could not be disturbed, and since there was not even a message for him he continued his journey. A fortnight later Airy acknowledged Adams's note and after referring to his calculations as based on 'assumed elements' (i.e., arbitrarily assumed values, which they were not and could not have been if they were the result of the inverse perturbation calculations), asked Adams whether his 'assumed perturbation' would explain the discrepancies between the distance Sun to Uranus given in Bouvard's tables and the observations.

Now the strange thing about the distance question is that if Adams's calculations were a solution of the inverse perturbation problem, the distance was bound to enter into the answer—one could hardly give orbital details without. Airy was a distinguished mathematician and would have been as well aware of this as Adams himself, so it seems obvious that he was still so sure that no one could solve the problem that he jumped to the conclusion that all Adams had done was to make a guess or two at an orbit and then worked out whether the perturbations would affect Uranus as they were observed to do. Adams had of course achieved the seemingly impossible and solved the problem backwards, working from the perturbations to the orbit, but this Airy failed to appreciate; indeed it is obvious that at this stage he had not even considered the matter, and herein lay the root of what was to become a *cause célèbre*. All might have been well if Adams had done more than present Airy with a brief note of his results, if he had given even a few words explaining how he had arrived at the figures, or if he had answered the question about planetary distance, however obvious the answer seemed. But it is always easy to be wise after the event and the fact is that Adams did not reply immediately: he waited until he had obtained even better figures for the orbit of the unknown planet and only then did he give Airy the answer he wanted. If Airy had spent a few moments with Adams instead of remaining firmly seated at the dining table, the procedure Adams had adopted would most probably have become clear and Airy would have instituted an observational search, for he was the most punctilious of men with a high sense of his duty as Astronomer Royal. However, it was obviously his belief that Adams had done no more than make a few inspired guesses that led him to consider the subject unworthy of upsetting his precisely arranged timetable.

How long Adams's theory would have remained unverified if nothing else had happened is impossible to say, but Airy was soon to receive a prod from another direction. This came from Leverrier who, in November 1845, presented a memoir to the French Académie des Sciences in which he discussed the discrepancies of Uranus's orbit. He had been invited to make his investigations by François Arago (1786–1853), then director of the Paris Observatory and the doyen of the French scientific community. An abstract from Leverrier's analysis was published in the journal *Comptes Rendus* and arrived in England in December, but so far there was nothing revolutionary in what he said and doubtless Airy and Challis merely congratulated themselves on seeing independent confirmation of what they knew so well. But Leverrier's memoir was only the first stage of his very thorough analysis of the problem. Six months later *Comptes Rendus* carried a second instalment of his work, and here he showed that no perturbations of any known planet could possibly account for the misbehaviour of Uranus. His mathematical analysis was thorough and penetrating and there could be no doubt whatsoever that an explanation must be sought elsewhere. There were, as will be obvious by now, only two alternatives: either universal gravitation was not universal or there was an undiscovered and unknown body in orbit beyond Uranus. The idea that Newtonian laws did not apply Leverrier, like Adams, rejected, and he cast out, too, such other face-saving explanations as had been proposed: suggestions that Uranus was retarded in its orbit because it was accompanied by a giant satellite, or travelling through a cloud of thick gas or other resistive substance. His analysis also demolished the belief held by a few astronomers that one orbit would fit the earlier pre-discovery observations and another the more recent ones, in the hope that they could assume that a comet or some such body had collided with Uranus and moved it from one orbit to another. There was nothing for it but to suppose that there was a yet undiscovered member of the solar system. Leverrier now had to solve the inverse perturbation problem and this he managed to do: as a mathematician he was Adams's equal and although he did not find the task any easier than Adams had done, he had the benefit of rather longer experience in the field of celestial mechanics. Leverrier was also able to devote himself to the work unhampered by the kind of distractions that had beset Adams, so that by the time the second *Comptes Rendus* was published, he too was able to give a position for the unknown planet.

This second, and to almost every astronomer, quite revolutionary result reached Airy late in June and he found that the position given by Leverrier was the same, to within one degree, as the position that Adams had provided eight months before. Airy later admitted[3] that he now felt no doubt of the accuracy of both calculations, but he wrote to Leverrier and asked the same question about the hypothetical planet's change of distance during its orbit as he had asked Adams. Leverrier replied at once, giving a long detailed explanation and expressing the hope that Airy, unlike Arago, would have enough confidence in his observations to institute an observational search for the planet. But Airy had a trip to the Continent planned and took absolutely no steps before he left to have any member of his Greenwich staff even so much as look for the planet in the predicted place. This was most odd, for he had just attended a meeting of the Board of Visitors to the observatory and had stated that there was every likelihood of discovery since Leverrier's and Adams's calculations agreed so closely. Why then he took no action is a mystery, and it can only be presumed that he had his own set of priorities in which a search for the predicted planet played no great part; doubtless he would have taken some action in due course, but only when he felt that time could be spared from what he must have imagined were more serious matters. The whole trouble with Airy was that he treated mathematical predictions, such as those of Leverrier and Adams, as a mathematical exercise, and he was always seeking some other justification of their results: ' ... exactness of results', he later told Leverrier in a letter,[4] 'is a matter of moral than of mathematical evidence'. By moral he meant the kind of evidence that seems to be right from a physical point of view—in other words a mathematical result by itself is of no significance unless the scientist has a 'moral' conviction that it fits in with the physical facts of nature. It would seem that Airy's neglect of Adams's results was due to this attitude of mind: here were cleverly contrived figures—just how cleverly contrived he did not appreciate—but they appeared to have no *physical* basis, there was no philosophical argument to support them such as Leverrier supplied with his reasoned rejection of all other possible explanations.

But if this was an excuse for delay it was hardly an argument for neglect after Leverrier's results arrived, and this was most probably pointed out to Airy by his old tutor Peacock when he went to Ely to stay with him. Peacock held the Lowndean chair of astronomy and mathematics at Cambridge and his opinion must have been the kind Airy would be unlikely to brush aside: at all events it was while at Ely that he wrote to Challis at the university observatory and asked him to begin searching for the planet. Airy chose the Cambridge observatory

127

because he himself had been director there and knew its equipment from first-hand experience. The observatory boasted a refractor with an object-glass of 25-inch aperture—at the time one of the largest refractors in the world—and if anything was able to pick up the trans-Uranian planet this telescope certainly would. And typical of Airy, he not only requested Challis to look for the planet, but also sent him detailed instructions of precisely how he should do this and offered him an assistant from Greenwich. Peacock had so alarmed Airy that whereas in late June he had made no attempt to do anything, now, ten days later, he was telling Challis[5] that 'the importance of this inquiry exceeds that of any current work which is of such a nature as not to be totally lost by delay'. But Challis had his own ideas about how to undertake the search, although he did agree with Airy that he should sweep an area of sky 30 degrees wide and 10 degrees deep—a tragic admission of lack of faith in the work of mathematicians—and estimated that the whole programme would take at least 300 hours of observing time or, roughly speaking, eight weeks if the weather were favourable. The search was on, even though Challis was now only doing in September 1846 what he should have begun a *year* before if he had had any faith in Adams's work: but 'it was so novel a thing to undertake observations in reliance on merely theoretical deductions'[6] as he later put it, that (in spite of Adams's outstanding and unique results in the tripos) he had to be pressed from outside before he would give a moment of telescope time to the task. Once started, Challis plodded along, charting all the stars, excepting the very dimmest, that his telescope could pick out, and in two months he had catalogued more than 3,000 stellar positions. This was all he could do, unless he was willing to accept the values of Adams and Leverrier and concentrate on the patch of sky in which they had forecast the planet would be seen: then, a few nights and his task would have been over. As it was there was no alternative but to catalogue every wretched star and, once this had been done, go over the observing again to find which, if any, showed a marked shift in position. It was a most tedious task, as Challis and Airy both knew.

All might have been well if Challis had not taken so long and had been able to announce a discovery, coupling Adams's name with Leverrier's; but his slow sweeps of the selected area

John Couch Adams from a photograph taken about
1846.

Urbain Jean Joseph Leverrier.

George Biddell Airy, the seventh Astronomer Royal.
(*Ronan Picture Library*)

of sky took so much time that Leverrier was able to make another solution of the mathematical equations and again come to a new position for the unknown planet, which was very close to the position given by Adams's second solution. Unwilling to wait for Challis to complete his work or, as seems more likely, unaware that anything at all was being done, Leverrier sought help elsewhere. And here it is only fair to state that French observers were as lethargic as those in Britain; in fact they were worse, for not one observatory set even a small instrument to search in Leverrier's computed section of the sky, and in spite of Arago's keenness that Leverrier should tackle the mathematics of the Uranus discrepancies no action whatsoever was taken at the Paris Observatory to confirm the results by observation. Just as much as Adams, Leverrier found himself up against a brick wall of conservatism: mathematics was all very well in its place but the Airy attitude of disbelief in pure mathematical predictions of physical facts seems to have been a mental affliction on both sides of the Channel.

Fortunately Leverrier did not let matters stand still, for unlike Adams he was neither reserved nor unassuming, and he remembered a young assistant at the Berlin Observatory, Johann Galle (1812–1910). In 1845 Galle had just received his doctor's degree and had sent Leverrier a published version of his dissertation on a comparison of observations of stars, the Sun and the Moon by various eighteenth-century astronomers; and as Leverrier had never acknowledged the gift he now decided, a year later, to make amends and, at the same time, ask Galle to examine the sky and see whether he could detect the disturbing planet. Galle was flattered to receive such a request from a man who already had a considerable reputation and asked Johann Encke for permission to undertake the search. Encke looked on his assistants as drudges, employed to do only what they were told—an attitude similar to that prevailing at Greenwich—and it was some time before Galle's persistence could prevail. Before he started, Galle received a plea from Heinrich d'Arrest (1822–1875), another and more junior assistant on the Berlin staff, to be allowed to help him in what had at least the appearance of being something more than mere routine, and he agreed. They were to use a most beautifully fashioned refractor of 9 inches aperture and Galle trained the telescope on a precise point in

I

the sky. Leverrier had predicted that they should see an un-mistakeable disk—the hall-mark of a planet—but not quite a thousandth of a degree in apparent size, and since the telescope was quite capable of showing this, Galle looked with great care, while d'Arrest watched with mounting excitement. But there was nothing to be seen, the field of view was cluttered with nothing but stars. Perhaps Airy and Encke were right, perhaps after all the exercises of mathematicians were no more than juggling with figures which had little if any counterpart in reality: perhaps there was no disturbing planet acting on Uranus.

Whether if he had been alone Galle would then have given up the search and reported his failure to Encke we do not know, for it was d'Arrest who now proved his worth. There was, he told Galle, a new chart of this very part of the sky which they ought to use, since then they could sweep a little further afield in safety, without getting lost amongst the plethora of stars. Galle was doubtful about star charts: he had recently used one prepared by Karl Harding that was supposed to show all the 'fixed' stars and so render it possible to detect extra bodies like the asteroids, and he knew the errors that this chart contained. All the same they went to the chart cupboard, and in an untidy drawer they found the chart they were looking for. Prepared as one of the charts of the Berlin Academy's new star atlas, it had been printed almost two years before but had not yet been published. It gave the Berlin astronomers an advantage over Challis: no longer did they have to contemplate trying to find the equivalent of a needle in a haystack, for they now possessed a chart which purported to give the precise location of every stalk of hay. Galle returned to the telescope and began to call out the appearances and positions of the stars he saw, while d'Arrest checked them on the chart, and they had not gone very far when they found a discrepancy; the telescope showed an object that d'Arrest was certain should not be there. As yet they could not be certain that this was Leverrier's planet, since it was not in the precise position he had computed—there was a dif-ference of almost a degree—and it was almost impossible to be sure whether it had a disk or not. However d'Arrest excitedly called Encke and the three of them stayed up watching the object until the early hours of the following morning; but still they could not detect sufficient movement of the interloper to be sure that it was not a star missed by Carl Berniker, compiler of the chart.

With what supressed excitement the three men waited for dusk the next night we can only imagine, but as soon as they could observe the object their doubts were resolved. It had moved in the direction that Leverrier had predicted it would, it had moved by almost the correct amount, it displayed a disk just about the size he claimed it should, and its position was less than a degree from where he had said it should be. The date was 24 September 1846. Encke announced the discovery of the new planet—incidentally omitting d'Arrest's name from a credit for the observational work—and the whole scientific word blazed with the news. Leverrier was lauded to the skies and Arago, never one to miss an opportunity for patriotism, called the discovery one of the most magnificent triumphs of astronomical theory, one of the glories of the Académie des Sciences and one of the noblest claims of France to the gratitude and admiration of posterity.

But exactly a week after Encke had made his announcement and while everyone was still eulogising Leverrier's triumph, John Herschel fired the first salvo of a battle that was to tear the astronomical world apart. In a letter to the *Athenaeum* magazine, Herschel, after duly praising Leverrier, pointed out how much there was a need to have some corroborative evidence of the mathematical calculations and then went on to say that when he had given his presidential address to the British Association in Southampton a month earlier—well before the actual Berlin discovery—he was well aware 'that a similar investigation had been independently entered into, and a conclusion as to the solution of the new planet very nearly coincident with M. Le Verrier's arrived at (in entire ignorance of his conclusions) by a young Cambridge mathematician, Mr Adams, who will, I hope, pardon this mention of his name (the matter being one of great historical moment), and who will doubtless, in his own good time and manner, place his calculations before the public'.[6] To this Challis added a second broadside, for two days later he wrote to Arago suggesting that the new planet should be called 'Oceanus', and informed him that he had himself been engaged in looking for the planet and had done so without success until he had read Leverrier's last memoir of late September and had then seen the planet, recognising it by its disk. But Challis did not say that the reason he had been looking was because of Adams's calculations: Adams's name was not mentioned. As yet there was no open hostility since the *Athenaeum* was not read widely, if at all, by continental scientists, and Challis's ambiguous letter could clearly be taken as a confirmation that Leverrier's achievement was what had put him on the right road—why he should have been looking for the planet in the first place does not seem to have raised any curiosity in a country wild with excitement about the discovery itself. Moreover if such curiosity had been awakened there were always Leverrier's earlier comments and memoirs about a new planet to fall back on—Challis's hint, for doubtless that is what he intended it to be, was too obtuse.

The battle only began in earnest when in the middle of October Airy wrote to congratulate Leverrier. He began in effusive terms: 'I was exceedingly struck with the completeness of your investigations. May you enjoy the honours which await you, and may you undertake other work with the same success and receive from all the enjoyment which you merit.' Then came the bombshell: 'I do not know whether you are aware that collateral researches have been going on in England and that they led to precisely the same results as yours. ... You are to be recognised beyond doubt as the true predictor of the planet's place. I may add that the English investigations, as I believe, were not quite so extensive as yours. They were known to me earlier than yours.'

Now the fat was truly in the fire; the hint in Challis's letter was seen to be more than it appeared on the surface as soon as he began to explain unequivocally that it was Adams's researches that had led to his looking for the planet. And ironically enough, while Challis gave credit to Leverrier for leading him to the actual discovery, it was only cloud that had prevented him from finding it earlier from Adams's evidence. Some little time before Galle's observations, Challis had been discussing his own work over dinner with another Cambridge don, William Kingsley. Kingsley was so interested when Challis told him that he thought he had seen an object which displayed a disk that he suggested they both go and look. Challis agreed and up to the observatory they went, but on the way they were delayed by

132

Mrs Challis who insisted that they had a cup of tea, and by the time they arrived at the telescope, cloud obscured the sky. It is not certain precisely when this happened, but it was definitely before news of the Berlin discovery reached Britain and only goes to show how little imagination Challis seems to have brought to bear on his work. Now, however, he was in the thick of what was to prove a very unsavoury battle. John Herschel's letter came to the attention of the French, and both Leverrier and Arago replied. Leverrier was upset and angry and appealed to Airy since, naturally enough, he could not understand why, if Airy had known all about the matter earlier, he had not said anything in his previous correspondence. Nor could he understand why Adams himself had neither said nor published anything, and why Challis had apparently been afraid of openly mentioning anything in his letter. Obviously the whole matter had a very unpleasant odour and smacked very much of a complete fabrication. Arago made no bones about how he felt, and in the *Comptes Rendus* he wrote:[8] 'No. No, the friends of science will not permit the consummation of such crying injustice. Journals and letters received from several English philosophers prove to me that, in that country also, the rights of our countryman will find zealous defenders. In conclusion, Mr Adams has no right to figure in the history of the new planet, neither by a detailed citation, nor even by the slightest allusion.'

The next step was obviously to clear the air and make all the facts known in a proper fashion, so as well as continuing a correspondence with Leverrier, Airy prepared a statement for the Royal Astronomical Society. Originally just the Astronomical Society, this body of professional astronomers and amateurs with astronomical interests had been founded in 1820 in the teeth of opposition from the Royal Society, or rather from its president Sir Joseph Banks, who thought that the existence of other scientific societies would curtail the power of the Royal. Banks had objected to the founding of the Royal Institution two decades earlier, and of the Geological Society in 1807, but it was generally thought that having lost those battles he would have mellowed a little in his attitude. With this in their minds John Herschel, Babbage, Peacock and others set about the formation of the Astronomical Society and at the beginning of 1820 persuaded the Duke of Somerset, sixth son of George III, to become its first president. Banks severely attacked Pond, the Astronomer Royal, for daring to be party to the plan, but from all accounts Banks received as good as he gave, and having no success at Greenwich went to work on Somerset. Somerset had not only accepted the presidency but had been attending a meeting, and what pressure Banks brought to bear on a man who was his close friend we may never know; but ten days later Somerset wrote that he felt himself 'obliged to resign the flattering hope of connecting my name with the labours of the Astronomical Society',[9] and William Herschel, then eighty-two, agreed to accept the office provided he did not have to attend meetings. His 40-foot telescope was adopted as the 'coat of arms' with the motto *'quicquid nitet notandum'* (everything that shines must be observed). As on the previous occasions Banks's aggressive attitude did nothing but make the embryonic Society stand firm and defy him to a man. Banks died four months later and opposition seems to have ended, so much so indeed that when in 1830 the Society applied for a royal charter this was granted with no more than the usual delays.

The main purpose in founding the Society was to organise a co-operative endeavour to chart the entire sky down to the dimmest object by repeated observations—an obvious extension of the work of the two Herschels and as laudable as it was impracticable with the equipment available at that time—but otherwise its aims were more modest but no less important, namely to act as a forum where scientific papers could be read and their contents discussed. It was this aspect of its activities that made it so suitable a place for airing all the facts about the Adams/Leverrier controversy, an airing that was sorely needed since British astronomers and even the public at large were expressing incredulity that Airy could have known the facts for so long and done so little and, in addition, that Adams should have sat by and been content that his work should remain unpublished. If Adams had achieved what was claimed, surely someone—Airy or Challis at least—should have advised him not to delay publication even if he was too retiring in character to do so on his own. Airy and Challis had come in for some very outspoken censure by the time the Royal Astronomical Society meeting was held in mid-November and it must have been a more than usually tense moment when Airy was called on first to give his 'Account' of the matter.

Perhaps because of his peculiar philosophy against a purely mathematical discovery like Adams's, devoid of any such 'physical' arguments as Leverrier had given, or possibly because of a desire to protect himself as much as he could, Airy spent most of his time eulogising Leverrier; all Adams received was an honourable mention. This surprising exhibition was followed by Challis, who was in the most awkward position since he had to explain why, when he had the means to make corroborative observations at his disposal in September 1845, he had persistently done nothing until the dilatory Airy actually prodded him into action ten months later: no wonder he wrote to Airy ten days before the meeting, 'I am in difficulties about this report and should be glad to see some means of getting out of it'.[10] He cut a sorry figure, but his account was open and frank. Challis was followed by Adams, who criticised himself for his delay in answering Airy's question about the unknown planet's orbit: there was neither rancour nor complaint in what he said and a contemporary claimed that he behaved 'like a bashful boy'. Fortunately one of those present was W. S. Stratford, then Superintendent of the *Nautical Almanac*, and it was owing to his efforts that Adams's address was printed as an appendix to the edition applying to 1851, published in 1847, and was thus given world-wide circulation. It is also worth recording that Adams's account was circulated by Heinrich Schumacher in the German periodical *Astronomische Nachrichten*.

The sanguine reader would no doubt imagine that Adams now received due if tardy credit, but no such thing happened. The French, Arago in the lead, demanded that the new planet should be renamed Leverrier, Leverrier himself suggesting *pari passu* that Uranus should be rechristened Herschel; and in Britain the Royal Society, which should have been a model of equity, gave its highest honour, the Copley medal, to Leverrier. In their prevous history they had made joint awards on eleven occasions, but it was not until 1848 that they repented and awarded it to Adams too. The record of the Royal Astronomical Society was not much better, for when Council met they could not agree about a joint award either, and it was only their regulations that prevented a second *faux pas* and ensured that in such a case no medal at all was awarded. By 1848 Council felt uneasy; clearly they must do something about the discovery of Neptune, as it had become known, and in the end they decided on the extraordinary course of issuing testimonials and for some reason best known to themselves gave a total of a dozen, some to their own members, one to Leverrier, another to Adams, one each to John Herschel and Airy, but nothing to either Galle or Challis.

Adams remained at Cambridge until 1852 when his fellowship expired, and he applied for the post of superintendent of the *Nautical Almanac* made vacant by Stratford's death. He was refused, but five years later was appointed professor of mathematics at St Andrews University. Cambridge almost immediately repaired their error and he took Peacock's chair as Lowndean professor, and in 1861 succeeded Challis as director of the observatory. Here he remained until his death in 1892, dealing with the mathematics of planetary, satellite, and especially lunar motions. His modesty prevented his accepting a knighthood and his retiring nature the post of Astronomer Royal which he was offered on Airy's retirement. Happily, though, Adams's early promise held good throughout his life and his work on celestial mechanics was outstandingly successful. With his work, the advantage gained by continental mathematicians in the previous century was to some extent cancelled out. After all the hubbub was over, he and Leverrier remained on the best of terms, and perhaps his character was shown at its best when, many years later, he was invited to add his name to the signatures in the front of a memorial album the Royal Society was presenting to Louis Pasteur, for beneath his name he wrote '*Hommage au Compatriote de Le verrier*'.

VII

The Quest for Precision

THE SCIENCE OF astronomy has many strands, but no matter which of these is the main concern of one decade or another, of this century or that, the one common thread that runs through is the demand for accuracy in observation. Only by an uncompromising attitude to errors of observation and imperfections in the most carefully made equipment is it possible to ensure that of all the exact sciences, astronomy is the peer. This concern with precision goes back a long way, and even in the sixteenth century Tycho Brahe examined, measured and made allowance for the kind of faults that not even the best instrument maker could avoid. In the eighteenth century this almost pathological concern for accuracy began to bear fruit, not only in the matter of the determination of longitude and the consequent evolution of the marine chronometer, but also in the quest for stellar parallax—that elusive shift of the nearer stars against the backcloth of the more distant ones, caused by the annual movement of the Earth in its orbit round the Sun.

Attempts to measure parallax had been made by many astronomers but none had been successful. In 1714 the elder Cassini (1625–1712), first director of the Paris Observatory, believed that at last he had achieved the almost impossible and obtained a value for the very bright star Sirius, but Halley disproved his result. Other attempts were made but it was James Bradley (1692–1762), the third Astronomer Royal, who had the first success; although it was not stellar parallax that his obervations revealed but a motion that needed to be known and accounted for if parallax was to be proved a physical reality. Bradley, a nephew of the eighteenth-century astronomer James Pound, collaborated with his uncle in making careful observations of the positions of objects like Jupiter's satellites and the extent of the beautiful system of rings that surrounds the equator of the planet Saturn. His work brought him early recognition: at twenty-five he was elected a Fellow of the Royal Society and three years later he was appointed to the Savilian chair of astronomy at Oxford.

In 1725, four years after his Oxford appointment, Bradley began a research programme with Samuel Molyneux (1689–1728), a brilliant amateur telescope maker. Molyneux had been impressed by not only Cassini's measurements but also the efforts of Hooke, who, unwilling to let any new idea pass him by, had in 1669 made a series of measurements of the star Gamma Draconis that appeared straight overhead from London. By observing a star at so high an altitude, Hooke hoped he would be able to reduce the effects of the Earth's atmosphere on the accuracy of his measurements. In this his reasoning was sound, for when a star is observed overhead, the light from it passes through a thinner layer of air than when it lies close to the horizon, and so is less disturbed by air currents and by distortions due to the air itself. With an overhead star the measurements he made of its position with reference to other stars would have every likelihood of being far more accurate than those made at any other angle, and since he noticed a shift in position he thought that what he measured might well be parallax. Molyneux decided to repeat this experiment and he commissioned George Graham to instal a long focus refracting telescope on his estate at Kew. The upper pivot—for the telescope could be moved a little from absolute verticality—was fixed to a chimney breast and the tube pointed out through a hole in the roof: the eyepiece lay in a room twenty-four feet below; the tube itself passing from the roof through holes in the floorboards. The instrument was ready early in December 1725 and Molyneux began his observations with Bradley assisting. They chose the same star that Hooke had used over half a century earlier and after they had been at work for a fortnight, Bradley noticed that the star had shifted position. To obtain a measurable shift in fourteen days was too good to be true, and they again observed the star meticulously. It was a delicate measurement to make, but Graham had built the instrument so carefully that there was no possibility of failing to be sure precisely where the star appeared in the sky. The shift was certainly real and it seemed that Hooke might well have been right when he suspected that his own observations showed a change: but was this a measure of parallax? If it were, then at the rate the star was shifting it must be rather nearer the Earth than expected.

The effect became more puzzling as observations progressed, for if they were really observing the long-sought stellar parallax, then for the star in question they should see the greatest shift in one direction in December and in the opposite direction in June. Yet this is not what happened. There was a shift, but its maxima came in March and September, and Bradley was left in no doubt about having to make another careful investigation. He continued to make further observations, first at Kew and then, after James Pound's death, at his widowed aunt's house at Wanstead where he installed a new 'zenith sector' telescope. His results showed him that the shift was no illusion; it waxed and waned perfectly regularly, yet always at the 'wrong' times. Moreover with the new telescope at Wanstead Bradley was able to observe other overhead stars and see whether, at their zenith passage, they too exhibited a shift. He found that they did and all with the same rhythm as in the case of the first star: maxima were always in March and September and never in June and December, so in these cases also the shift was certainly not due to parallax.

Bradley puzzled over the nature of the shift he had observed, and turned over in his mind every conceivable explanation: yet an analysis of the effects of the Earth's atmosphere, and even the possibility of an additional and hitherto unknown motion of the Earth, failed to provide a solution that would fit in with the observed facts. The clue to the answer came to him while he was in a boat on the Thames. He noticed that every time there was an alteration of course the pennant on the mast suddenly changed direction. On reflection he realised what every sailor knew, that the change in direction of the pennant was only an apparent effect, due not to any alteration in the direction of the wind but to the change of course of the boat, and he then began to apply this experience as an analogy of his astronomical observations.

The shift of the star was periodic and changed in direction every six months, so clearly it must be due to a motion of the observer on a moving Earth. With this established he had then to seek for something that acted in place of the constant direction of the wind and after a little thought he came to the decision that the one constant equivalent was the beam of light sent by the star to his telescope. Light, he knew, took time to travel through space—this had been proved by Olaus Römer in 1675 —and so he began to calculate what effect its time of travel would have on his observations. For consider a beam of light entering the front of the zenith telescope and travelling straight down it. To pass along the tube from the object-glass at the top down to the eyepiece at the bottom the light would take a certain amount of time—a very short time it is true, since the velocity of light is exceedingly fast, but a specific interval nevertheless—and if the telescope were still, it ought to pass straight down without any deflection at all: if the beam entered the centre of the object-glass, then it should emerge in the centre of the eyepiece. But suppose that while the light is passing from the centre of the object-glass the whole telescope moves, say to the right, then the light will continue passing in the same straight line down the tube—but now it cannot end up in the centre of the eyepiece because the centre of the eyepiece has moved (to the right): in consequence, the place where light arrives will lie somewhere to the left of the eyepiece centre. And what the observer will see is a star image that appears to have shifted to the left; indeed he will be able to measure this displaced image quite precisely.

When Bradley calculated out the kind of displacement he should obtain in theory, taking into account the length of his telescope, the speed of light according to Römer's measurements, and the velocity of the Earth in its orbit (computed from Newtonian theory), he found that his actual observations agreed very well indeed. This 'aberration of light' was obviously of significance if measures of stellar parallax were to be successful and it would have to be taken into account in all cases of refined measurement, but it also had another important aspect: it was the first observational proof that the Earth really does move in space. As Bradley put it in his paper in *Philosophical Transactions*:[1] 'There appearing therefore no sensible parallax in the fixed stars, the Anti-Copernicans have still room on that account to object against the motion of the earth; and they may have (if they please) a much greater objection against the hypothesis by which I have endeavoured to solve the forementioned phenomena, by denying the progressive motion of light, as well as that of the earth'—a backhanded slap in the face for those who would clearly now have to deny a well accepted phenomenon of physics as well as a widely agreed theory of astronomy.

But Bradley did more than merely publish his result and point out its relevance to the doctrine of a moving Earth: he also discussed the problem of stellar parallax itself and tried to clear away any illusions astronomers might have about the magnitude of the problem that still faced them. In the paper just quoted he wrote, ' ... the parallax of the fixed stars is much smaller than hath been hitherto supposed by those who have pretended to deduce it from their observations. I believe that I may venture to say, that in either of the two stars ... [I have observed] ... it does not amount to more than 2" [2 seconds of arc]. I am of the opinion that if it were 1" I should have perceived it ...' Now one second of arc is a very small quantity indeed, amounting to no more than 1/3,600 of a degree, or, to put it in more ordinary terms, the apparent size of a pinhead viewed at a distance of some 225 yards. That the early eighteenth-century astronomer could measure to such a degree of precision is astounding, but if one consider's Bradley's statement that even this was not sufficient, the immensity of the problem can be more fully appreciated.

In view of Bradley's proven ability as an accurate observer it was natural enough that when Halley died in 1742 his recommendation that Bradley ought to succeed him was accepted, and early in the year Bradley moved to Greenwich. As we have seen (Chapter IV), Bradley obtained new instruments and in due course, after his nephew left, a formally recognised assistant. Two men acted in this capacity, first Charles Mason (1730–1787) and then Charles Green (?–1770), both of whom were to obtain some distinction in their own right: Mason went to America with Jeremiah Dixon (*fl.* 1763) to survey and mark the boundary between Maryland and other counties, laying down the Mason-Dixon line, while Green went to the South Seas with Captain Cook. Bradley made a host of careful observations that were of considerable use to later generations of astronomers in determining the proper motions of stars, but he did not neglect

141

his work with the zenith sector, nor did he lose his ability to speculate with remarkable perspicacity. In 1748, for instance, he anticipated William Herschel's use of pairs of stars for parallax movement, and discussed the possibility of a proper motion of the Sun. As for his zenith measurements, he made further investigations on aberration and found yet another apparent movement. Analysis of this led Bradley to realise that the new shift was also regular, although it was slower than the aberration displacement and only repeated itself every eighteen years; he correctly interpreted it as due to a rocking or 'nutation' of the Earth's axis, and since its period was the same as that of the rotation of the whole orbit of the Moon, he realised that the Moon was the primary cause.

Bradley's quest for precision was indefatigable. He kept his observing instruments in as perfect adjustment as possible, he drew up tables of the apparent displacement of stars by the Earth's atmosphere, and he even allowed for the atmospheric effects due to the temperature and barometric pressure of the air. His observations were outstanding and led the French astronomer Jean Delambre to say of his work that it raised Bradley 'above the greatest astronomers of all times and countries'.[2] This was an exaggeration, made in the late 1820's before the actual discovery of parallax, and his stature is perhaps better expressed in the words of his present successor:[3] 'the greatest astronomer who has ever held the office of Astronomer Royal in nearly three centuries'.

In the observational records at Greenwich, under the date 16 July 1762, the following entry appears: 'Dr Bradley exchanged this life for a better at Chalford, in Gloucestershire, July 13, 1762. Aged 70'; and the books contain no further records, since the observations were still considered the personal property of the Astronomer Royal. Bradley's successor was Nathaniel Bliss (1700–1764), whose sole claim to fame seems to be that the only known portrait of him is engraved on a pewter tankard under the edifying inscription 'This sure is Bliss, if Bliss on Earth there be'. But then he held office for no more than two years, and although he followed Bradley's example he had too little time to leave any permanent mark on the observatory.

The work of Greenwich in the eighteenth century under Bradley, Bliss and Maskelyne was of an increasing standard of precision and in this it followed the same course as astronomy at other national observatories. Both Bradley and Maskelyne improved the instrumental equipment and the buildings. In 1811 Maskelyne died and was succeeded by John Pond (1767–1836), whom he had recommended and who had been making careful measurements from his own private observatory. It was during his twenty-four year reign that ever more accurate equipment was introduced, most notably two instruments built by Edward Troughton (1753–1835), an excellent London instrument maker. With these Pond began to make more accurate observations, taking into account every conceivable instrumental error in a way never before achieved; and it was during his time that the Astronomer Royal's salary was increased to a more realistic figure and that the number of assistants grew from the inadequate to the workable. Pond was permitted to employ six men, but his unfortunate attitude to them is best expressed in his own words:[4] 'I want indefatigable, hardworking, and, above all, obedient drudges (for so I must call them, although they are drudges of superior order), men who will be contented to pass half their day in using their hands and eyes in the mechanical art of observing, and the remainder of it in the dull process of calculation.' This was a fatal mistake, for men looked on as drudges were hardly likely to be interested either in their work or in the reputation of the Observatory; and although Pond devised cast iron rules of procedure, the programme did not flourish as it should, especially when, towards the end of his tenure, he was frequently away through failing health.

In 1833 Pond's catalogue of the positions of 1,112 stars was completed, a catalogue that contained more stars really accurately pinpointed than any other available at the time, and it was said that this work put the science of positional astronomy more in debt to Pond than to all his countrymen put together since the time of Bradley. But the admirable observations were not coupled to a good or even workable administration. This was due partly to Pond's own attitude, partly to the gross inefficiency of his chief assistant, and partly to Pond's increasing ill health, as well as to the time spent at the observatory testing and providing certificates for marine chronometers. Moreover, Pond took little interest in the *Nautical Almanac*, and it was in 1818 that the post of Superintendent had to be created, a post quite separate from that of Astronomer Royal and not then under his jurisdiction. Clearly this was not likely to ingratiate the Astronomer Royal with the authorities—they had raised his salary but appeared to be getting less for their money—and it is not surprising that the Lords Commissioners of the Admiralty, who had taken control of the observatory in 1818, began to remonstrate with Pond. Finally he resigned towards the end of 1835.

Pond's career ended sadly considering the excellent work he had initiated; and when he died the next year the Admiralty declined to continue payments to his wife, who was in great financial distress. It was only owing to the protestations of his successor, Airy, that they had a change of heart. Airy, whom we have earlier seen in a less favourable light, was generous in his praise of Pond and pointed out to the Admiralty what his predecessor had achieved at Greenwich: his regularity in observing (so essential for long-term accuracy), his attention to fundamentals and the removal of errors, and his methods of observation. 'In comparing Mr Pond's systems of observation with Dr Maskelyne's, no one can avoid being impressed with the inferiority of Dr Maskelyne's.'[5] On the other hand Airy was, as always, scrupulously fair and declined to bestow praise where, in his opinion, it was not due: 'Mr Pond understood nothing of physical astronomy; but neither did anyone else in England'[5] —a clear indication of what Airy thought of the state of celestial mechanics in Britain at the beginning of the nineteenth century. Nevertheless his strong and balanced report obtained its end and Mrs Pond was looked after.

Airy was the firm administrator that the observatory needed. He sacked the inefficient chief assistant of Pond's day and replaced him by Robert Main (1808–1878), a good Cambridge mathematician; he reduced the amount of time and effort expended on checking chronometers, since he found 'much of the business had no connection whatever with astronomy';[6] and he began to devise forms that could be completed by observers so as to give results which were consistent, easier of analysis and less likely to have errors. He did not spare himself to make Greenwich efficient once again, and yet at the same time he continued to keep a tight grip on the work he had done at the

The main gateway to the Royal Observatory in Greenwich Park, *c.* 1880. This photograph shows the public electric clock installed by Airy in the outside wall, and on the roof of Flamsteed House the time ball (right) and meteorological instruments (left).

(Ronan Picture Library)

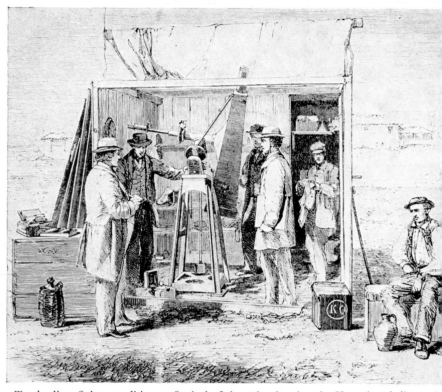

Total eclipse Solar expedition to Spain in July 1860, showing the Kew photoheliograph with its designer Warren De la Rue (left). On this occasion De la Rue took the first successful photographs of a total solar eclipse. The British expedition was led by Airy.

(*Ronan Picture Library*)

university observatory at Cambridge. Here he had co-operated with Stephen Groombridge (*fl.* 1816), a keen and able amateur who lived at Blackheath and had a small observatory with some of Troughton's precision equipment, the observatory being next to his dining room so that he could conveniently leave his dinner, observe a star position, and then return to his meal. It was through Airy's care that Groombridge's catalogue of more than 4,000 stars close to the north pole of the heavens was corrected and republished while he was Astronomer Royal, and as late as 1837, two years after his appointment, we still find Airy writing in autobiographical notes:[7] 'My connection with Cambridge Observatory was not yet finished. I had determined that I would not leave a figure to be computed by my successor.' But if Airy drove himself hard, he did not spare his assistants either. Observers were often on duty for twenty-one hours at a stretch, while the boys who had to carry out the routine arithmetic on the observations were kept at their desks from eight in the morning untl eight at night.

After the slackness under Pond, Airy was determined that there should be none while he was in charge. This almost amounted to a mania and sometimes led him to extraordinary behaviour. There was the time when he spent the entire afternoon writing 'empty' on large cards to be nailed to a heterogeneous collection of packing cases because he had noticed confusion and waste of time when they were mixed with others containing equipment of one kind or another. Then there was the occasion when he set some of his assistants away to Harton Colliery to measure the behaviour of a pendulum deep under ground in an attempt to determine the change of gravity with depth; he not only told them precisely which trains to take and where to change as if they were children going on their first journey alone, but he also packed up soap and towels with the instruments so that they were sure to have everything they required. There is also a story that very late at night, and whether or not it was raining, he often went with a lantern into the observatory buildings and called on the assistant on duty. 'Ah, you're there. Good.' Airy would say and then return to his quarters satisfied that the staff was present and correct—even if bad weather prevented work.

Airy was a creature of habit. His day was punctiliously

K

timed: from nine until half past two he worked in his own room, unless it were summer when he would often start earlier, and after this long stint he would go for a brisk walk and dine about half past three, an early hour even for the nineteenth century, but prescribed by his doctor. A sleep followed dinner, tea followed the sleep, and from about seven in the evening until ten at night he would continue work, although now with his family around him. Cards and a book came next, then bed regularly at eleven. This routine continued for years and Airy studiously avoided going out to dinner parties whenever he could, although he never failed to provide a welcome for his friends when they came to Greenwich. His methodical nature ruled his life: he kept an account of all income and expenses, using double-entry book-keeping for which he had a passion, and he religiously filed every item of correspondence, every bill, every receipt and, towards the end of his life, seemed more concerned about putting each paper in its proper place than with mastering its contents.

Yet if Airy had his foibles and his failings, there is no doubt about his directorship of the Royal Observatory: under him it flourished and its buildings grew, its work expanded into new fields and its reputation was enhanced to such a degree that in the early nineteen hundreds the eminent American mathematical astronomer Simon Newcombe wrote:[8] 'The most useful branch of astronomy has ... been that which ... is practically applied to the determination of geographical positions on land and at sea. The Greenwich Observatory has, during the past century, been so far the largest contributor in this direction as to give rise to the remark that, if this branch of astronomy were entirely lost, it could be reconstructed from the Greeenwich observations alone.' And not only for mapping and navigation was the work of Greenwich of permanent use; its observations were, and are, of lasting value, especially in determining the proper motion of stars, for in most cases these can only be discovered by comparing careful and accurate positional measurements made at different epochs.

Airy understood extraordinarily well the methods to be used in this work and, equally important, the way in which they could be improved. When he became Astronomer Royal the practice was to use two separate instruments—the transit instrument and the mural circle—and to observe stars only when they were directly on the meridian. The transit instrument was a small telescope with its tube accurately pivoted in a north-south direction, and its purpose was to allow an observer to note the precise instant when a star (or the Moon or a planet, for that matter) was due south. The moment of transit was determined by observing the instant at which the celestial body passed through cross-wires mounted in the telescope eyepiece. The difference in timing between the transit of one body and another across the meridian permitted a very precise determination of their difference in position. But such observations only gave part of the information required—they only provided the difference in position in a left-to-right direction (in 'right ascension')—and the complementary facts of position difference in altitude ('declination') meant using also the mural circle or mural arc. These, as their name implies, were instruments mounted on the side of a wall, again facing due south, and they consisted of telescopes free to swing across a graduated arc, or pivot in the centre of a graduated circle. With them Halley, Bradley, Bliss, Maskelyne, and especially Pond, had achieved their valuable and surprisingly accurate results; but it was Airy who not only saw the necessity to economise in observing time if there was to be an increase in the work done, but also devised the means of achieving such economy. His solution, which in itself sounds simple enough, was to combine the two instruments into one and have a transit circle that would permit the instant of crossing the meridian to be observed and the declination of the body to be obtained at the same moment. But the practical problems were prodigious, for the instrument had both to lie perfectly in the meridian and also to carry measuring circles that would provide an unequivocal measurement of the tilt of the telescope tube and thus the declination of a celestial body. No one appreciated the technical requirements better than Airy and the surprising thing is that no one could design it down to the last mechanical detail better than he, for among Airy's accomplishments was the most profound mechanical and engineering knowledge. The 'Airy transit circle' was completed in 1851 and from the time of its installation until after the Second World War, a period of close on a century, the instrument was in regular

147

use. This, if nothing else, is a tribute to Airy's extraordinary abilities as an instrument engineer.

There was one other requirement that positional measurements at Greenwich needed to satisfy, and that was observation of the same accuracy off the meridian as on it. In Flamsteed's day there was equipment to do this, but when Airy began his reign the observatory possessed nothing to measure with the extra precision then needed, and he therefore set about solving this problem also. The outcome was an 'altazimuth' telescope which, as he designed it, was essentially a transit circle that could be turned to any point in the heavens; and although simple in principle, it had to be built with an extraordinary degree of precision if it were to match the standards of the new transit. The need for it was pressing and measurements were important, not only because they were able to supply the necessary facts when cloud obscured a meridian passage, but because they could supply information about the Moon when in other parts of her orbit.

It was during Airy's directorship that the Royal Observatory began to venture into new fields. In 1840, five years after his appointment, regular meteorological and magnetic observations began to be carried out in a special new department. The excuse for doing both kinds of observation from what, after all, was essentially an astronomical observatory, was that both the weather and changes in the Earth's magnetism have an indirect effect on navigation. This is true, and although Airy was more interested in the effects of meteorological change on the accuracy of his astronomical observations, it was this indirect influence on navigation that justified his request to establish the department. The magnetic side needed less excuse, since the mariner must be able to rely on his magnetic compass and to do this he needed to know how much from true (geographical) north it pointed. In Halley's day the fact of variation in the direction in which a magnetic compass points was well known, but there are many factors at work that determine how great this variation shall be. Clearly the mariner must know of these changes and an observatory like Greenwich, with its unique collection of instruments for determining true north and south, was in an ideal position to discover precisely the amount of magnetic variation at any time; it was also alone in being able to assess other factors that seemed to cause a host of minor variations—variations due to the Earth's rotation and its orbital motion round the Sun, variations caused by the movement of the Moon and even by physical conditions on the Sun itself. Indeed it was the effect of the latter that led Airy in 1837 to propose, and the Admiralty to accept, that the observatory should have is own solar department in which regular observations of the Sun's physical condition could be made. Some thirty years earlier Heinrich Schwabe (1789–1875) in Dessau had discovered that there is a regular cycle of change in the number of dark spots that appear on the solar surface, and ever since links between the change in sunspot numbers and variations in terrestrial magnetism had been found. By the time Airy wanted his solar department, telegraphic communication was well established and the power of a large sunspot to disrupt telegraph services was known; there was obviously a need to investigate the whole question more fully.

While Airy was busy at Greenwich, careful observations were being made at other observatories to try to detect stellar parallax. In South Africa, at the Cape of Good Hope, Thomas Henderson (1798–1844) was trying his hand at detecting a parallax for the very bright star Alpha Centauri which can only be seen in the southern hemisphere. Henderson, an attorney's clerk from Dundee, had done useful work as an amateur and when in 1831 William IV established an observatory at the Cape, Henderson was appointed to direct it. He stayed only two years and did not begin his observing programme until April 1832, yet in the short time he was there, and in spite of inadequate equipment, he managed to make a series of worthwhile measurements. One of the things he determined to do was to correct the catalogue position of Alpha Centauri and, finding that it possessed a larger proper motion than its surrounding stars, he conjectured that this might well mean it was comparatively close to the Earth: so he set about examining his observations for any evidence of parallax. But Henderson was a cautious man, careful never to commit himself on anything until and unless he was absolutely sure, and when he left South Africa for Scotland in 1833, he took his observations with him to mull over. In 1834 he took up his new appointment as Astronomer Royal for Scotland at the Royal Observatory at Edinburgh. Here Henderson studied his results with the greatest care and after a number of years finally concluded that Alpha Centauri certainly had a parallax and that this amounted to one second of arc.

But he was loth to publish until he had corroborative evidence, and it was not until a Lieutenant Meadows at the Cape confirmed the one second residual shift that he was prepared to face the world with his new and vital evidence. At last, on 9 January 1839, Henderson announced his result, but it was now too late for him to claim priority of discovery, for just two months earlier Friedrich Wilhelm Bessel (1784–1846) announced a parallax for the star 61 Cygni. Bessel had been led to study 61 Cygni for the same reasons that Henderson had tackled Alpha Centauri—its large proper motion—and for his observations he had the advantage of a new design of refractor constructed by a German, Joseph von Fraunhofer. Fraunhofer fashioned his lenses out of the superb optical glass that was made by a Swiss, Pierre Guinand, at Bendiktbeuren in Bavaria: he mounted his instruments on a convenient form of equatorial stand, but his greatest innovation was that he equipped this particular telescope with a heliometer. Originally devised in 1754 by an Oxford man, Servington Savery, the heliometer was first constructed by a French optician, Pierre Bouguer, and consisted of an object-glass divided across the middle: this gave two images, and by sliding one half lens across the other, the relative positions of the two could be displaced. It was an admirable way of measuring the diameters of the Moon, the planets, and especially of the Sun, since one edge of one image could be displaced until it coincided with the other edge of the second image. It was widely adopted for this kind of observation, since the Sun's glare prevented the satisfactory use of the ordinary cross-wire micrometer. For stellar observations it obviated the difficulty of determining when a dark wire lay precisely over the glaring image of a star, and with it Bessel determined a parallax that amounted to no more than one third of a second of arc, an astoundingly small value.

Modern observations, using more refined techniques, have confirmed Bessel's value and reduced Henderson's to about three-quarters of its original amount, but even so credit is due to both Bessel and Henderson for making the first successful

150

measures of stellar distance. For Alpha Centauri this works out at some 26,000,000,000 miles, or in modern terms four and one-third light-years, one light-year being the distance travelled by a beam of light during one year. The smaller parallax of 61 Cygni gives a value of almost eleven light-years. These distances are surprisingly great and their determination acted as a salutory shock to any astronomers who might have thought that the universe was not so very much larger than the solar system: in spite of Bradley's warning that he would have detected a parallax of one second of arc if such existed, the small parallax of 61 Cygni created a stir, and others began to hunt for parallaxes.

The measurement of a stellar parallax means using the diameter of the Earth's orbit as a base-line from which to measure the position of a star on two occasions six months apart (see Chapter V). The answer comes in the form of a very small angle, and if we are to convert it into miles or light-years to make it more intelligible, then the diameter of the Earth's orbit must be known to a nicety. Although Newtonian gravitation and Kepler's laws of planetary motion both provide a simple way of calculating the relative distances of the planets from the Sun by measuring the time each takes to complete an orbit, these only give a *ratio*: we may know that Neptune is thirty times further off from the Sun than we are or that our distance is two and a half times greater than that of Mercury, but what the specific distance is we cannot know unless and until the distance Earth to Sun is measured. From every point of view then, this basic distance—the so-called 'astronomical unit'—is of great significance, and even from Greek times attempts were made to determine it. In the seventeenth century French astronomers had tried to measure the distance of the Sun by first finding the distance of Mars and then computing the astronomical unit from Kepler's laws. They chose this approach because in parts of its orbit Mars lies closer to us than the Sun and any measurements of its distance will be subject to smaller errors. The method they used was to observe the planet from Paris and, at the same time, have observations made by a colleague who was a long but known distance away. The results were encouraging and gave support to another method strongly advocated by Halley throughout his career, namely to observe a transit of Venus.

151

Venus at its closest comes nearer to the Earth than to Mars, and about once every century comes in line with the Sun and the Earth, and then appears to cross or transit over the Sun's disk. By timing from a number of widely separated places the moments when the planet appears to touch each edge of the Sun's disk, it should in theory be possible to determine the distance of Venus with a very high degree of accuracy. Halley pinned his faith on the two transits (they are in pairs when they do come) due to occur in 1761 and 1769, and closer to the date astronomers in Europe began to make preparations. The French played the leading role in the 1761 transit, and even though France was at war with Britain diplomatic co-operation was arranged for so important a venture; although by comparison with France, Britain made little more than a half-hearted attempt to do justice to Halley's scheme. The French efforts were directed by Joseph Delisle (1688–1768), who had known Halley, and considerable help was obtained from astronomers working in Russia. Delisle spent much time simplifying the procedure Halley had suggested and tried it out on a transit of Mercury across the Sun that occurred in 1753, and although Mercury does not come so close to the Earth as Venus, the experience he obtained was valuable. In the event, the French co-ordinated observations made in Peking, Siberia, France and the Indian Ocean.

British astronomers were tardy in making plans and it was only in 1760 when Delisle's scheme became known that they started to get down to details. The reason for the lethargy was not any disrespect for Halley but rather a surfeit of individualism—astronomers were rebelling against too much organized direction, coupled with the unlikelihood of obtaining the necessary funds. However once Delisle's plans had arrived, the British moved quickly. The Royal Society took action and Mason and Dixon were dispatched to Sumatra, Nevil Maskelyne with an assistant, Robert Waddington, to St Helena; John Winthrop (1715–1779) and a small party went from Harvard to Newfoundland very much of their own volition, while Bradley observed at Greenwich. Mason and Dixon never reached Sumatra, but ended up at the Cape, and made their observations from there using explicit instructions drawn up by Bradley. Maskelyne and Waddington had bad weather and although they made a few observations these were of little use, but Winthrop was luckier.

For the 1769 transit another series of expeditions and observations was organised: a total of one hundred and fifty observers, thirty more than in 1761, were busy and the spread of the observing stations over the Earth's surface was just a little wider than before. Experience gained in the first transit was put to good use in the second, but there was one factor that even the best of observers could not overcome and this was the phenomenon that has the unedifying but descriptive title of the black drop. Its cause is that when Venus is seen against the Sun, it presents a jet black disk in the telescope, since we are viewing the dark side of the planet, the bright side being that facing the Sun. As the Sun is very bright, there is an enormous contrast between the Sun and the planet, so that the eye plays tricks and there seems to be a black 'bridge' connecting the edge of the Sun with the black disk of the planet. The planetary disk then appears to be shaped like a dark raindrop and it becomes virtually impossible to determine the precise moment when the planet actually makes contact with the Sun's disk. All the same, the results of this vast international undertaking proved to be useful, even if not as accurate as had been hoped; and in 1824 when Encke analysed the results, a figure of ninety-five and a quarter million miles for the Sun's distance was obtained. This was certainly a better observation than any made before, although Pierre Laplace had found a value very similar in 1787 when he had analysed the perturbing effects of the Earth on the Moon and the planets, and computed the astronomical unit from this.

Other attempts were made, and in 1877 David Gill (1843–1914), like the French two centuries before, measured the distance of Mars. Gill, a Scotsman, was an astute observer who, in 1879, was to take over the Cape of Good Hope Observatory. He discussed the whole problem of using Mars with Airy and agreed to travel to Ascension in the South Atlantic. Here, with a base-line of some fourteen hundred miles to Greenwich, observations were made that gave a distance of just over ninety-three million miles for the Sun, a smaller but more correct value than that given by the 1761 and 1769 transits. However, astronomers did not abandon the idea of using transits of Venus and

153

when these occurred again in 1874 and 1882 a host of observations were again made. This time, however, they used the new invention of photography to record the results in the hope that the black drop would be less troublesome with a camera than with the human eye. The first two attempts resulted in a value of ninety-two and a half million miles, and now matters were coming to a head: each new determination was closer in value to the one before and it was growing obvious that the development of observing techniques was leading to an evaluation that would stand for many years ahead.

The discovery of the minor planets in the early years of the nineteenth century at first did not appear to have any relevance to the problem of determining the Sun's distance. In 1898, however, the minor planet Eros was unearthed after an examination of a host of photographic plates taken at Harvard a few years earlier, prompted by a clue from Gustav Witt (1866–1946) of Berlin. Using the Berlin and Harvard evidence it was found that the orbit of this tiny body did not lie wholly between those of Mars and Jupiter but was so eccentrically placed that for part of every journey round the Sun it travelled between Mars and the Earth. The outcome of this discovery was that astronomers had a new object which they could observe and one that came closer to the Earth than any other, except for the Moon which was not suitable for the obervations they required. Just after its discovery Eros approached to within something like twenty-five million miles; fifty-eight observatories scattered over the world took advantage of the fact and a vast number of measurements were obtained. These required careful study and analysis if they were to be used for calculating the astronomical unit, and it fell to Arthur Hinks (1873–1945), an assistant at the Cambridge University observatory, to undertake the long and laborious task. Hinks himself had joined in the observing programme, taking photographs by the hundred during the few clear nights when Eros was at a close approach—an experience that further convinced him, as well as other astronomers, of the usefulness of photography at the telescope as a tool for precise measurement. But although the photographs had been taken quickly, their analysis and the analysis of the thousands of visual observations was less easy, and it was not until 1910 that he could announce the Sun's distance as 92,811,497 miles; this was the most accurate figure ever obtained, since Hinks specified the possible error at no more than 31,300 miles one way or the other.

The value of photography for increasing accuracy in measurement had not been realised immediately it was discovered and it was Hinks who proved its value once and for all. This he did not only by his measurements of the Sun's distance but also because he applied it to the whole problem of stellar parallax, reducing the errors in measuring the exceedingly small angles involved to hardly more than one hundredth of a second of arc, an accuracy undreamed of in the days of Henderson and Bessel who could only make laborious optical observations. But if it took time to appreciate the use of photography for measurement of very small angles, it was early realised that the camera could be used as an aid to observing, and within a few years of Louis Daguerre's (1787–1851) invention in 1837 of a truly practical way of taking photographs on a copper plate, the French successfully took pictures of the Sun and George Bond in America managed the more difficult task of photographing the Moon. The disadvantages of daguerrotype were that it needed inconveniently long exposures to record even such a bright object as the Moon, and the pictures could not be copied. If matters had not improved it is doubtful whether photography and astronomy would ever have become the inseparable partners they now are. However, photographic techniques did not remain static and in Britain experiments were already being made by William Fox Talbot (1800–1877), an artist of no great talent who used the camera lucida as an aid in preparing his outline sketches. Fox Talbot's approach to the problem had been to return to some experiments made at the beginning of the century by Humphry Davy and Thomas Wedgwood, son of the famous potter. Davy and Wedgwood had made shadow pictures on light-sensitive paper, but since they knew of no way of preventing these from fading rapidly while one looked at them, the discovery had no practical use at all. Fox Talbot was a little more successful since he could make photographs that lasted a reasonable time: they were still not permanent, but as they were taken on paper copies they could be made at will. His work came to the notice of the ubiquitous John Herschel, who coined the terms negative and positive for the paper photographs and the pictures duplicated from them (as well as the word 'photography' itself), and it was he who in 1819 finally managed to 'fix' them permanently.

Fox Talbot's results not only meant that copies could now be made of an original photograph but also that the exposure time was much shorter. However, there was still a disadvantage: the negatives were on paper and all paper has a certain amount of grain, so there was a limit to the amount of detail that could be recorded, and better results were needed for scientific work. Something more transparent was required and glass was an obvious choice; but here was an apparently insurmountable difficulty, for it seemed impossible to bond a light-sensitive surface to anything so smooth and prevent it washing away during the long drawn-out business of photographic processing. The difficulty was overcome, but not until 1851, when a British chemist, Frederick Scott Archer (1813–1857), introduced a glass plate covered with collodion. Collodion, invented a few years earlier as a protection for wounds and burns, took well to glass and provided a shorter exposure photographic layer when mixed with the appropriate light-sensitive chemicals. The only drawback to the process was that the plates had to be used in a camera as soon as they had been coated and then chemically processed immediately afterwards. They were such an advance over anything previously available, giving exposures which had no longer to be measured in minutes, than in spite of the necessity for a darkroom to accompany the camera at all times, the wet collodion plate ousted all competitors and held the field alone for the next twenty-five years. Unhappily Scott Archer never reaped his full reward, as he and his wife died six years after he devised the process, but it is at least something that the British government granted a pension of £50 per annum to each of his three orphaned children.

Photography was now in a position to act as a useful tool for astronomy and it was first extensively applied by Warren De La Rue (1815–1889). De la Rue was a manufacturing stationer and as with many men of his day, science was his spare-time occupation: but if he was an amateur it was in the true sense of the word. At the Great Exhibition of 1851 he saw photographs by Scott Archer and a daguerrotype of the Moon, and these

156

intrigued him to such an extent that he determined to see what he could achieve himself. In 1853 he managed to take successful photographs of the Moon, and by the next year was gaining some reputation among professionals. When John Herschel, ever at the forefront of new ideas, suggested that a photographic 'patrol' of the Sun should be made it was to De la Rue that everyone turned, and he designed a special photographic tele-scope—a photoheliograph—with funds from the Royal Society. This instrument caused a minor sensation, for it took photo-graphs with exposures of no more than a fraction of a second. In 1860 De la Rue took it with him to Rivabellosa in Spain and not only obtained the first photographs of a solar eclipse, but, incidentally and no less important, managed to capture the images of prominences—those flame-like protruberances which are now known to be composed of extremely hot hydrogen gas but which at the time were a cause of speculation. Airy led this expedition—indeed it was he who persuaded the Admiralty to place the Himalaya at the disposal of a party of sixty British and foreign astronomers—and he was greatly impressed with De la Rue's work, writing: 'The eclipse was fairly well ob-served: I personally did not do my part well. The most impor-tant were Mr De la Rue's photographic operations.' From Airy this was high praise indeed. The photoheliograph was returned to Kew in due course, and for the next ten years De la Rue and Balfour Stewart (1828–1887), the observatory's director, made a series of thousands of photographs covering an almost com-plete sun-spot cycle. In 1783 the instrument was moved to Greenwich, where it was used to start the new heliographic department, and was in continuous use for the next two years until a new and slightly larger copy was ready.

Britain always seems to have been blessed with a host of talented amateurs, and De la Rue was only one of a number who began to use the new photographic techniques, although he was the first. Another brilliant and ingenious astronomical pioneer was Andrew Common (? –1903), a prosaic business-man who was attracted to astronomy when young, and is re-ported never to have been without a telescope. Common had a passion for large telescopes and after trying photography with a comparatively small refractor, he commissioned George Calver, a manufacturer of very fine and very large silver-on-glass mirrors, to construct one for him of 18 inches diameter to be fitted into a telescope of Common's own design. With this Common took some good pictures of Jupiter, but his ambitions were still unsatisfied and he commissioned Calver to build a new mirror twice the size; as he did not agree with the instrument makers of his day, he again designed the mounting. The new telescope was highly successful, Common's enthusiasm knew no bounds, and he decided to try to obtain pictures of the nebula in Orion. Attempts to photograph this hazy object had already been made in the United States by Henry Draper (1837–1882) and in France by Pierre Janssen (1824–1907), but their results neither satisfied them nor did they really delineate the fainter parts, and it was Common who in February 1883 took the first pictures of any quality. As a contemporary historian commented:[10] 'Photography may thereby be said to have definitely assumed the office of historiographer to the nebulae, since this one impression embodies a mass of facts hardly to be compassed by months of labour with the pencil, and affords a record of shape and relative brightness of the various parts of the stupendous object it delineates, which must prove invaluable to the students of its future condition.'

Common's success was to a great extent due to the mounting he had designed and his method of driving the telescope to follow the stars in their procession across the sky. It was so accurate that he was able to make exposures of an hour or more, and with the new highly sensitive wet collodion plates, they allowed the dim but fine details to be seen quite clearly. Common now decided to build a yet larger telescope and ordered two 60-inch glass disks from France; one was cast with a hole in the centre so that the light beam could be directed back down the tube and allow the observer to work at an eyepiece conveniently placed behind the main mirror—the optical system designed by Cassegrain—and one was solid so that observations could be made from the front of the tube in the more usual way. Common built the telescope with the solid mirror, but when he fell some twenty feet from the front of the tube he decided never to use it that way again. He had now to fashion the second mirror, but encountered immense difficulties because the glass casting was far from perfect, and it took him five years of patient work to obtain an acceptable result: this telescope was the world's largest silver-on-glass reflector. Unfortunately at this point Common's interest was side-tracked into designing telescopic sights for the British army, so that on his death in 1903 this giant instrument was lying in his garden uncared for and forgotten.

However, if Common's greatest telescope proved a disappointment, his 36-inch lived on to make a new name for itself in the United States. In 1885 he sold it to Edward Crossley, a Halifax merchant, who began to use it but found the Yorkshire climate unsuitable for so large a telescope: for proper use at full aperture it needed clear and steady air. The Director of the Lick Observatory in California persuaded Crossley to donate the instrument to the observatory and in 1895 it began work under the clear skies of western America. At the time it was the largest reflector in the United States and with it James Keeler took a wonderful series of celestial photographs, which, like Common's own work and that of another well-to-do British amateur, Isaac Roberts, encouraged further the use of celestial photography. At his own private observatory equipped with a 7-inch refractor and a beautiful 20-inch reflector constructed and mounted by Howard Grubb, Roberts took celestial photographs of outstanding quality, among which were three-hour exposures of the galaxy in Andromeda; these showed only too clearly its spiral structure and at last revealed details of its construction that had foiled even the best optical observers. A further fillip for photography came in 1878 when Richard Maddox and Charles Bennett caused a revolution by devising and marketing highly sensitive dry photographic plates that needed no treatment just before exposure but could be taken out of their box, used straight away, and then developed at leisure.

It was amateurs who led in the field of astronomical photography; but the professionals soon appreciated the importance of a technique which with its long exposures could build up images and make it possible to observe stars that were far too dim for the eye to see through a telescope. There was one professional who saw even further than this and realised the camera's potentialities for saving laborious hours at the telescope spent in charting the sky, although he hit on the idea quite fortuitously. David Gill, now Her Majesty's Astronomer at the Cape, decided on the spur of the moment to take photographs of a comet that suddenly appeared in the early autumn of 1882; it was bright enough to be visible even in daylight—as Gill said,[11] it showed 'an astonishing brilliancy as it rose behind the mountains on the east of Table Bay ... seemed in no way diminished in brightness when the sun rose a few minutes afterward.' Gill at once arranged for a local photographer to fasten a camera to one of the telescopes, and the results, taken at night, showed not only the comet but a host of nearby stars: it was the images of these that convinced Gill of the possibilities of photography as a means of charting the sky.

At about the same time, two astronomers at the Paris Observatory, Paul and Prosper Henry, were busy revising a star atlas, and they decided that they must use photography if they were to chart the Milky Way as they wanted: they therefore set about designing a suitable telescope and, by 1885, were able to announce their preliminary results to the Académie des Sciences. With Gill and the Henrys things began to move. Admiral Mouchez, director of the Paris Observatory, was converted, discussed matters independently with De la Rue, and then co-operated with Gill in calling an international conference in Paris. The outcome was a scheme for liaison between eighteen observatories scattered widely over the world, to take something of the order of 20,000 photographs covering the entire sky and prepare a chart to be known as the *Carte du Ciel*. Although there was more enthusiasm than application, much of the chart was completed and the contributions of Greenwich and the Cape were incorporated.

Before we leave the question of precision measurements, something must be said about one important concomitant to any determination of position, and that is the problem of the accurate measurement of time. It was Christiaan Huygens in the seventeenth century who worked out the theory of the motion of a pendulum and determined the theoretical factors involved in its isochronism—its ability to complete every swing in precisely the same amount of time. But there was a vast difference between theory and practice and although pendulum clocks were constructed, their accuracy was not good enough for astronomy. The advent of John Harrison's chronometer was a revolution not only in determining longitude but also because its success emphasised the importance of compensating for changes in temperature in the surroundings; yet this was only a beginning in the development of even more elaborate forms of compensation and of clocks with an accuracy that is nothing short of phenomenal.

To begin with, however, Greenwich was concerned primarily with the purely practical problem of providing not only a testing and adjusting service for marine chronometers, but also a time distribution service which would enable mariners to correct their chronometers before they set sail. To this end a time-ball was set up at the observatory in 1833, during Pond's term of office. The ball, about five feet in diameter and painted red, was fixed on the top of Wren's original building (Flamsteed House), and was free to move up and down a mast some twelve feet high. The Lords Commissioners of the Admiralty, who instituted the service, gave notice on 28 October that:[12]

'. . . . a Ball will henceforward be dropped, every day, from the top of a pole . . . at the moment of one o'clock P.M. mean solar time. By observing the first instant of its downward movement, all vessels in the adjacent Reaches of the river, as well as in most of the Docks, will thereby have an opportunity of regulating and rating their Chronometers.

'The Ball will be hoisted half-way up the pole, at five minutes before one o'clock, as a preparatory signal, and close up, at two minutes before one.'

Mean solar time was what we now call Greenwich Mean Time: it is a regular clock time computed from the rotation of the Earth and not from simple observations of the movement of the Sun, which varies its rate of motion across the sky at different seasons of the year.

Nothing further in the way of time distribution could be achieved until some means was available for disseminating signals more widely, and even with the invention of the telegraph in the late 1830's the observatory had to wait until commercially viable systems had been established. By the 1850's the situation had altered enough for Airy to install eight electric clocks at Greenwich, and to arrange for them to transmit an appropriate electric signal not only to the observatory time-ball but also to a duplicate set up in the Strand in London by the Electric Telegraph Co.; while in 1853, a further time-ball was

161

installed at Deal and later on in many Admiralty dockyards. Moreover Airy had one of the electric clocks installed at the gates of the observatory and also despatched hourly time signals all over the railway telegraph system. The advent of the telegraph certainly facilitated the distribution of accurate time, but there is an interesting story showing what happened before this, when chronometer makers needed a time check against which they could compare their manufactures. One of the senior assistants at Greenwich, Henry Belville, a refugee from the French Revolution who was known at the observatory as 'Mr Henry', had charge of a chronometer that was checked against the observatory standard and then trundled round to the various clockmakers. On his death the Admiralty permitted his widow to carry on the work as a means of livelihood, and on her death the privilege passed to her daughter, who from 1892 until 1940, twice a week, compared her father's chronometer watch, constructed by John Arnold in 1791, with the Greenwich standard and then took it to chronometer makers

In Airy's time, also, an electromagnetic method of recording transit observations was initiated at the observatory. The device was of American design and consisted of a large drum around which a sheet of paper was rolled and a pen operated by an electromagnet. The pen drew a line on the drum as the latter rotated, but was given a small movement every second by an impulse from an electric clock, so that when the paper was unrolled the line would be seen to be broken at regular intervals by small pip marks. In addition to the regular pips the pen was also connected by a pair of wires to a switch held in the observer's hand so that as a star transited over a crosswire, he could close the switch and record another pip on the paper. This 'chronograph' increased the accuracy of timing considerably and, interestingly enough, underlined a problem that had faced previous Astronomers Royal—the problem of 'personal equation'. This is now well appreciated to be a physiological factor which results in one observer's reactions being faster or slower than those of another, so that in timing a transit, for instance, no two observers will ever be able to put a mark on the chronograph at precisely the same instant, even though the differences between them may be no more than a fraction of a second. Allowance can be made for each individual's personal equation and so the error is nowhere near as serious as it sounds: like all errors that arise in accurate measurement, steps can be taken to eradicate them once they are known and their cause recognized. In Maskelyne's day the problem was not appreciated: finding that his assistant David Kinnebrook persistently observed a star transit later than he himself Maskelyne concluded, quite wrongly that Kinnebrook was lazy and failing to apply himself to his duties with proper zeal; scoldings, warnings and exhortation having no effect, as indeed they could not, Kinnebrook was sacked as incompetent—and Maskelyne missed a golden opportunity to discover a source of error that remained unknown until some thirty years later.

The increase in precision which occurred during the nineteenth century was phenomenal. Errors in position measurements were reduced by some forty-five times, and in the measurement of time by a factor of ten, even better than Harrison's achievement. In addition new observatories were established and some astounding advances were to be made in methods of probing the nature of the universe.

VIII

The Chemistry of Space

THE GROWTH OF astronomy in Britain in the nineteenth century saw the expansion of the observatory at Edinburgh, and in Ireland of those at Armagh and Dunsink. The Edinburgh observatory had roots going back to early in the previous century when Colin Maclaurin (1698–1746), the professor of mathematics at the university, attempted to raise funds by delivering public lectures; but his project was abruptly terminated by the '45 rebellion, during which he helped defend the city and contracted a disease that cost him his life. James Short, the instrument maker, also tried to awaken interest, but died prematurely, and it was only through the efforts of his brother Thomas, an optician of Leith, that the city fathers were at last persuaded to allow an observatory to be built in a quarter-acre site on Carlton Hill. Here with £400 from Maclaurin's trustees a Gothic style tower was constructed in 1766, equipped with some of Short's instruments, and opened to the public. After various vicissitudes the tower became dilapidated and the observatory might have faded into obscurity had it not been for the formation of an Astronomical Institution in 1811, which seems to have created considerable interest and certainly attracted a substantial amount of money. The tower was repaired, a transit house was built for positional measurements, and there were proposals for a more extensive professional observatory and the foundation of a 'physical cabinet' where members might experiment. A great fillip was given to the whole project when George IV visited Edinburgh in 1822 and decided it should have the status of a royal observatory, a fillip that had a practical as well as a prestige side, for the British government provided a grant of £2,000 for instruments. But the astronomical finances of Scotland were still very slender and the Institution was finally forced to hand over the administration to the government. In 1834 the government appointed the over-cautious Thomas Henderson as the first Astronomer Royal for Scotland and professor of astronomy at Edinburgh. Under Henderson things began to move and by the end of his ten years in office the observatory was a flourishing concern; his successor Piazzi Smyth (1819–1900) took control in 1846, two years after Henderson's death.

Smyth was a very different personality from Henderson and seems to have had two separate sides to his character. On the one hand he was a competent astronomer who, on an expedition to Teneriffe in 1856, not only advocated the now accepted practice of mounting large telescopes on high ground where the atmosphere is clearer for observing, but also made measurements of the heat of moonlight, finding that it was half that obtained from a candle at a distance of fifteen feet—an interesting if rather esoteric result. On the other hand Smyth had a predeliction for what may charitably be called mystical astronomy, and took more than a passing interest in the Great Pyramid of Giza: he looked on this not only as a tomb constructed for astronomical observations but also as a monument that contained within its walls a clue to mankind's past and future. However, if Piazzi Smyth's interests were not always of the highest scientific value, his measurements of lunar heat at least set a seal on observations on the physical characteristics of the universe which were followed by his successor Ralph Copeland (1839–1905). Copeland came over from Lord Rosse's observatory* and made various useful studies with the spectroscope—a device that we shall be discussing in some detail presently. It was during Copeland's directorship that the observatory moved from its home at Carlton Hill to Blackford Hill, a new site outside the city where it had more room and also the benefit of an endowment from Lord Crawford. Since then its work was continued under a succession of Astronomers Royal for Scotland of high ability, one of whom, Frank Dyson (1868–1939) was translated to Greenwich as the ninth Astronomer Royal; it has undertaken programmes of careful time determination, but ever since Copeland's day its main research

* See p. 112 *et seq.*

165

programmes have been concerned with the study of the physical conditions of the stars.

In Ireland astronomy also receive encouragement, from Lord Rokeby who became Archbishop of Armagh and Primate of all Ireland in 1765 and from Francis Andrews, a lawyer and provost of the University of Dublin in the 1780's. At Armagh the observatory was completed by 1790 and the meticulous observer James Hamilton (? –1815) was its first director. Little seems known about Hamilton, whose directorship was marked by no particular distinction except for the story that two of his wards frequently entertained their admirers in the observatory building. Equipment was scanty, not because of any parsimony on the part of the archbishop but through the covetous attitude of his descendants, who on his death countermanded all orders for new instruments; so that two clocks, and a small equatorially mounted telescope by Troughton and a small transit instrument were all that the observatory possessed. With a new Archbishop who took no interest in astronomy, the outlook was bleak. All the same it is to Hamilton's credit that he managed to measure some star positions which were later published by Pond. Hamilton died in 1815 and his successor did little astronomy and nothing to enhance the observatory's reputation. However in 1823 Romney Robinson, who was an extraordinary character, had also been an assistant to Rosse, was appointed director and held the post throughout a great part of the nineteenth century, for he was not succeeded until early in 1882. When Robinson took over the observatory was in a parlous state, but the new Primate took little persuading to finance proper equipment and grant a stipend suitable for a man without substantial private means. Under Robinson's directorship the observatory began to make its mark and in 1859 a catalogue of more than five thousand star positions was published; this enormous catalogue was Robinson's chief astronomical work, but it should be recorded that he also established regular meteorological observations, invented the cup anemometer for determining wind speed, measured the difference in longitude between Armagh and Dublin with great ingenuity by timing the flashes of small rockets launched from both places, and with great vigour successfuly fought the encroachments of local railway lines that threatened to destroy any future work at the observatory. Unhappily the observatory's funds were drained away in 1869 with the passing of Gladstone's proposal to disestablish the Irish Church, since the funds came entirely from Church income, and for the rest of his tenure the work that could be done was seriously curtailed.

Robinson was succeeded by John Louis Emil Dreyer (1852–1926), a Dane who for a time worked as assistant to Lord Rosse and under whose control the observatory flourished. Dreyer extracted financial support from various secular sources and then settled down to acquiring new equipment, his primary efforts being spent in obtaining an excellent refractor of 10 inches aperture built by Howard Grubb of Dublin: with this he made a re-examination of all nebulae, star clusters, galaxies and any other hazy objects that he could detect. This work was a sequel to the research he had carried out with Rosse and, collated with further observations by Rosse and a new assistant, it led to the now astronomically famous *New General Catalogue of Nebulae* (1888) which contained more than eleven hundred objects in addition to those discovered by and catalogued by John Herschel at the Cape between 1834 and 1839. Financial difficulties again beset Armagh and the only scientific grants Dreyer could obtain were small and not really adequate for the work he wanted to do. Observing was continued, but at less effective pace, and in 1916 Dreyer resigned his position to move to Oxford. There he devoted himself to the monumental task of analysing the observational results and life's work of his sixteenth-century compatriot Tycho Brahe, an undertaking for which historians of science will ever be in his debt.

In the south of Ireland, Francis Andrews' legacy to the University of Dublin was a munificent, £3,000, together with £250 per annum for building and endowing an astronomical observatory; but almost at once difficulties arose. Andrews's family contested his will—criticising the legacy for the observatory which they called as a 'purely ornamental institution—and a compromise was reached which left the funds rather depleted. Even so, the university decided to pursue its intention to build an observatory: a site was chosen at Dunsink within 'reasonable walking distance' of Trinity College, a building contract placed, and Henry Ussher (? –1790) appointed to the new chair of astronomy. In three years the buildings were up, instruments installed—some to Ussher's own design—and observing commenced, but Ussher died within five years. He was widely mourned, for he appears to have been greatly loved as a man even though he had no great standing as an astronomer, and the university provided money for a bust, a prize essay (title 'The Death of Ussher'), and the publication of his astronomical work and of his extensive sermons. The sermons never appeared, the observations remained unpublished, no prize essay was judged, and even the bust did not materialise: but there was considerable competition for the vacant chair and the observatory's directorship. The University decided to appoint the Rev John Brinkley (1763–1835) a Cambridge man, instead of the Irish candidate, and after a storm of criticism had subsided honour was satisfied by the issue in 1792 of Letters Patent by George III ordaining 'for ever hereafter a Professor of Astronomy, on the foundation of Dr Andrews, to be called and known by the name of the Royal Astronomer for Ireland'.

Although this sounded very well, the observatory which Brinkley now directed was not adequately equipped and a large mural circle that the university agreed should be constructed by Jesse Ramsden in London had not materialised. The project had been initiated in Ussher's day and Ramsden, then the doyen of British instrument makers, had by his enthusiasm persuaded everyone to agree to his constructing a giant mural with a graduated circle ten feet in diameter—a gargantuan undertaking which would have given Dunsink the largest instrument of this kind in the world and the possibility of making superb measurements. But the high hopes of Ussher, Ramsden and the university authorities were unfulfilled. Ramsden found that the ten-foot circle was too large even for him to construct, and he tried a nine-foot circle with equal lack of success, settling in the end for one of eight feet in diameter which was still far larger than anything else he ever made. The trouble Ramsden experienced caused inordinate delays: the instrument, commissioned in 1785, was uncompleted seven years later when the Board of Visitors to the observatory enquired about it, and seven years after this it had still not appeared. It was now 1799, and in 1800 when Ramsden died feelers were put out to Maskelyne at Greenwich to see not only whether the order could be completed but also to enquire whether the money already advanced on the project was lost beyond hope of recovery. Maskelyne was able to give them encouragement, for Ramsden's business was still flourishing under Matthew Berge, one of his workmen; Ussher was long since dead, but Brinkley was still waiting and hopes again ran high. In the event Berge was as slow as his quondam master, and seven years later Dunsink still awaited its giant mural; only in 1808, twenty-three years after the original order had been placed, did it arrive. Brinkley had himself waited eighteen years for it before he could begin observational work.

With such a series of procrastinations it is little wonder that in the next eighteen years Brinkley produced observations of little more than passing significance. His aims were high enough—he set himself the tasks of redetermining the measurement of aberration and mutation that Bradley had made (see pp. 178–185), and then of discovering stellar parallax—but in the end his ecclesiastical commitments took precedence, he was elected Bishop Berkeley's successor in the see of Cloyne, and a new director had to be sought. The choice fell on William Rowan Hamilton (1805–1865), a man equally brilliant in classics, oriental languages and mathematics, then still an undergraduate. But Hamilton found observing uncongenial, spent his energies on mathematics, and although his name gave lustre to the observatory it was not until the days of his successor Robert Ball (1840–1913) that practical astronomy moved into the ascendant once more. As at Armagh, Dunsink under Ball moved on to studies connected with the physical nature of stars and nebulae, a subject which at the end of the nineteenth century began to capture the imagination of astronomers the world over.

Analysing the physical nature of celestial bodies had its beginnings in experiments made in the early years of the eighteenth century by a young Scotsman, Thomas Melvill (1726–1753). Melvill, like Newton before him, was interested in the question of light and colours and wanted to investigate by what amount light of different colours was turned or refracted from a straight path by a prism. Melvill used a series of coloured flames as his source of light, generating them by burning substances like sea-salt in the flame of a spirit lamp, and he noticed that in every case he obtained a distinctive yellow flame which was invariably refracted to the same degree. It was almost half a century before his work was pursued, when Augustus de Morgan (1806–1871) and William Wollaston (1766–1828) in Britain, and Joseph Fraunhofer (1787–1826) in Munich repeated his experiments, and all three found that Melvill was correct. But Wollaston and Fraunhofer went further. First they passed light from the flames through a narrow slit before it entered the prism, and obtained an image which appeared as a narrow yellow line; they then measured this image a great deal more precisely than Melvill had done. Various other substances were tried, all giving the same yellow line, while Wollaston and Fraunhofer also noticed that when they compared the image obtained with a flame and the image obtained when they passed sunlight through the slit and prism, the coloured spectrum of the Sun was crossed by a number of dark lines.

Wollaston now seems to have lost interest in the subject, but in 1815 Fraunhofer devised a prism and slit with a more elaborate optical train of lenses and set about plotting as many lines in the Sun's spectrum as he could. Moreover with his new 'spectroscope' he was able to fix the positions of Melvill's yellow line with respect to the full coloured band of sunlight; but the cause of the lines and of the yellow line in particular was still as much of a mystery to him as to his British contemporaries. He observed the sunlight reflected from the Moon and planets and noticed that it contained the same dark lines as the original sunlight, but this did not help solve the mystery. Fraunhofer very nearly stumbled on the clue when he discovered that starlight also showed a coloured spectrum crossed by lines, often in different places from those in sunlight, but all he was able to do was to suggest that the lines owed their origin to the very nature of these bodies: it was in Britain that matters were next taken a step further.

The trouble with the early analyses was that no one could eliminate the yellow line whatever substance was used, and they could find no explanation for it. Fox Talbot (see also p. 155) tried hard to puzzle his way out of the problem and concluded that the presence in the spectrum of any particular coloured ray indicated the physical presence of some chemical substance— a view which, coupled with Fraunhofer's conjecture, might have opened up a new field of chemical analysis for astronomers as early as 1826. But although Fox Talbot and Fraunhofer found that the yellow line always appeared when the metal sodium was heated in a flame, they were put off by the fact that it was also evident when sodium was not present. For the next thirty years no one, including men of such ability as John Herschel and the physicist Charles Wheatstone (1802–1875), could come any closer to a solution. Then in 1856 many lines of enquiry seemed to converge: William Swan (*fl.* 1850) suggested that the inevitable appearance of the yellow line was due to the presence of sodium as an impurity in all the various substances that had been tried, while William Allen Miller (1801–1880), professor of chemistry at King's College, London, discovered that when he passed an electric current between pieces of metal in order to generate an intense electric light, and examined this light through a spectroscope, the bright coloured lines he obtained were different for different kinds of metals. All went to show that every chemical substance when heated until it glowed displayed its own particular characteristic bright lines: but it was one thing to believe that this was so and quite another to prove it. Chemists and physicists in Britain and on the Continent were all worrying at the problem, but it was in Germany in the University of Heidelberg that the final proof came in 1859, through a brilliant series of experiments by the physicist Gustav Kirchhoff (1824–1887) and the well known chemist Robert Bunsen (1811–1899). Their experiments were detailed, thorough and conclusive and they showed beyond all doubt that Swan, Fox Talbot and Miller were right—every chemical substance did possess its own characteristic colour lines in the spectrum. They did more than this, however, for they also found that the dark lines in the spectrum of the Sun coincided exactly in position with the bright lines given by chemicals when heated in a flame or by metal rods when burned with an electric current in an arc light. All the loose threads were now tied together, and the possibility of chemical analysis by heating substances and observing the result with a spectroscope was transformed into a certainty.

Kirchhoff and Bunsen had reached their final conclusions in two ways: first by passing sunlight through the bright flames of glowing chemical substances, and thus repeating an experiment

171

that Miller had carried out at King's; secondly by passing sunlight between the metal rods of an arc light, an experiment that had been tried successfully by Léon Foucault (1819–1868) in Paris. Unfortunately Miller had been content, like Foucault, with the simple fact that a coloured flame in the one case, and an electric arc in the other, had the power of stopping certain rays of sunlight; neither had delved just that much deeper and enquired why this happened. This is where Kirchhoff and Bunsen scored, but since they were interested only in chemical analysis in the laboratory they did not pursue any astronomical implications of their research: this was left for others—who turned out to be the British—to exploit to the full. The initiator of this astronomical research was William Huggins (1824–1910), a mercer living in south London who, surprisingly enough in view of what was to follow, had no formal scientific training of any kind. At the time of the Kirchhoff-Bunsen experiments he was thirty-five, and had sold the family business to devote himself to science with a particular emphasis on astronomy. He had his own observatory which housed a very fine refractor with an 8-inch object glass constructed by Alvan Clark, an American portrait painter turned optician, who was famous for his lenses.

Huggins's first thoughts about studying the spectra of celestial bodies came to him when he attended a soirée held by the Pharmaceutical Society in London. The new spectroscopic results discovered by the two Germans were all the rage and Huggins was intrigued beyond measure at the demonstration he saw; as he put it himself:[2] 'Just at this time, when a vague longing after newer methods of observation for attacking many of the problems of the heavenly bodies filled my mind, the news reached me of Kirchhoff's great discovery of the true nature and chemical composition of the Fraunchofter lines. This news was to me like the coming upon a spring of water in a dry and thirsty land. Here at last presented itself the very order of work for which in an indefinite way I was longing—namely, to extend his novel methods of research upon the sun to the other heavenly bodies.' Prompted by his enthusiasm he approached Miller at the soirée, suggested that they should return to his observatory at Tulse Hill together, and on the way told him of his desire and tried to enlist his support. To begin with Miller hesitated; the technical difficulties seemed to him almost insuperable, for he was well aware, as Huggins was not, that no apparatus then available was good enough to provide the kind of spectrum that was required if serious research on stellar spectra was to be undertaken, and told Huggins as much. The road ahead would involve them in much disappointment and if they were to be successful it would mean using every bit of ingenuity and all the perseverance they could muster. Huggins was adamant, however, and in the end Miller was convinced that he must do what he could to encourage this unknown but wildly idealistic amateur: although he could devote little time to the project himself, Miller had enough experience to realise that at least his moral support would be valuable—just how valuable even the most optimistic of men could not have foreseen.

The technical problems that faced Huggins were tremendous. 'It is difficult', he later wrote,[3] 'for anyone who has now only to give an order for a star spectroscope, to understand in any true degree the difficulties which we met with in attempting to make observations for the first time. From the Sun with which the Heidelberg professors had to do—which, even bright as it is, for some parts of the spectrum has no light to spare—to the brightest star is a very far cry. The light received at the earth from a first magnitude star, as Vega, is only about one forty-thousand-millionth part of that received from the sun.' Yet however impossible the task appeared to be, Huggins set about with a will, and explored all manner of techniques. Some of these including trying to form a spectrum of starlight using a hollow glass prism filled with a bisulphide of carbon solution, since this is very dense and has great power to disperse light into a well spread out band of colours, the very thing that was wanted. Yet the method had its drawbacks, as Huggins's reminiscences recall: 'I remember that for our first trials we had one of the hollow prisms filled with bisulphide of carbon so much in use then, and which in consequence of a small leak smelt abominably. To this day the pungent odour reminds me of star spectra!'[3]

The experiments were long-drawn-out and tedious, but Huggins never lost his enthusiasm. Piece by piece he began to build up a picture of the chemical constitution of the universe, commencing with the laborious task of mapping the bright lines to be found in the spectra of twenty-four chemical elements in the laboratory, and then going on to the unenviable labour of trying to observe the dim stellar spectra. But this was not all, for it was little use merely observing the spectrum of a particular star; he had also to identify each of the dark lines, and this meant having something with which to compare them so that their positions could be accurately mapped and matched with his standard spectra of chemical elements. To try to identify and chart the positions of the lines by observing over which colours in the spectrum they lay was too imprecise, for the colours fade into one another and there is no boundary that can be recognized. Huggins adopted the only practicable course (and one that has become generally followed), namely to have a device that could pass a standard light source into the spectroscope as well as starlight. To start with he used moonlight for his standard, but this was not satisfactory—it varied from one night to the next and was not always available—so he moved on to the use of a small electric spark, the spectrum from which he could obtain at leisure and as often as he required, and which was readily compared with his chemical standards. To achieve this, however, meant fitting a large electric coil and batteries near the eyepiece end of his telescope, and negotiating this massive equipment in the dark must have been quite hazardous —indeed when the apparatus had later been multiplied, Huggins found that there were some positions of his telescope at which he himself became jammed against the walls of his observatory. In 1863 the near chaos was increased almost to breaking point when he installed a developing tent inside his observatory as well, so that he could begin to take photographs by the wet collodion process. The results were not wildly successful, although they showed promise, but when in 1876 the sensitive dry plates arrived, Huggins gave up his visual observations and was able to use photography entirely. This gave him a great advantage not only in speed of observing but also in the accuracy with which the positions of the spectral lines could be determined.

But Huggins did not have to wait until the 70's before he had results valuable enough to announce, for as early as 1863, four years after he had started to tackle the problem, he and Miller

174

were able to present to the Royal Society a preliminary paper on the spectral lines of some of the brighter stars. On the same date as the Miller-Huggins paper was read before the Society, news of similar work by Lewis Rutherford (1816–1892) in the United States arrived, but Rutherford seems to have become side-tracked by the challenge of celestial photography and Huggins and Miller had the field almost to themselves: only Father Angelo Secchi in Rome and Hermann Vogel in Germany were then competitors. A year later Huggins and Miller were able to present a more extensive paper to the Royal, and this contained Huggins's vitally important and completely novel discovery about the nature of nebulae or, rather, about those nebulae which neither the Herschels, Rosse, nor any other observer had so far been able to resolve into separate stars. The object that had engaged Huggins's attention was one of those mysterious planetary nebulae that had so interested William Herschel: 'On the evening of 29th August', Huggins reported,[4] 'I directed the telescope for the first time to a planetary nebula in Draco. I looked into the spectroscope. No spectrum such as I expected! A single bright line only! At first I suspected some displacement of the prism, and that I was looking at a reflection of the illuminated slit. ... This thought was scarcely more than momentary; then the true interpretation flashed upon me. The riddle of the nebulae was solved. The answer which had come to us in the light itself, read: Not an aggregation of stars, but a luminous gas.'

By 1866 Huggins had examined the spectra of sixty nebulae and of these he found that one third were gaseous like the planetary nebula in Draco, but the remainder had star-like spectra and clearly must be collections of stars. These results were of the highest importance and more than any other began to show the immense power of the stellar spectroscope: it was a key that could unlock a hundred doors barred to the astronomer who possessed no more than a telescope and his own eyes as the sum total of his equipment.

Huggins's enthusiasm now knew no bounds, and every object was grist to the spectroscopic mill. The appearance of a bright comet in 1864 acted as a new stimulus and Huggins discovered that, like some of the nebulae, this possessed bright lines and so proved to be mainly composed of gas; later observations with improved techniques on fainter comets, however, made it clear that some of their illumination had a continuous spectrum crossed by dark lines and showed him that reflected sunlight also played its part. A nova that blazed forth in 1866 attracted his attention too, and in August of that year Huggins was able to deliver to the British Association a quite astounding analysis of the results of his first seven and a half years' work—indeed it was so profound and revolutionary that the results are worth quoting in summary. As far as the stars themselves were concerned, Huggins was able to state quite definitely that all the brightest at least had a structure similar to that of the Sun, and contained the selfsame chemical elements as are to be found on Earth; variable stars, he discovered, show changes in their spectra, which clearly indicated that their light variation was due to some physical cause, at least in those bright ones which had been observed; physical changes had also taken place in the nova of the previous May; true nebulae were clouds of gas and comets were composed of similar material—a series of outstandingly important discoveries.

In 1864 Miller found that the pressure of work at Kings College prevented him from co-operating further and for four years Huggins had to work alone, looking after his mother to whom he was devoted. In 1868 she died and for four months he was so overcome with grief that he was quite unable to continue his research or even to accept an invitation from Napoleon III to visit the Tuileries and tell him of his work. Yet by December 1870 he was recovered enough to go to Oran in an attempt to view a total solar eclipse, and although it was cloudy he thoroughly enjoyed himself, meeting other astronomers and among others the dynamic Pierre Janssen, who had extricated himself from beleaguered Paris by balloon. But perhaps his greatest encouragement came from the Royal Society, which had elected him a Fellow in 1865 and awarded him a royal medal the following year, for in 1869 the Council decided that Huggins would benefit from some new equipment and applied a £1,500 bequest to provide it: Huggins insisted that it must only be on loan so that it could be put to use by others when he was too old to use it to the full, and the Society agreed. The old observatory dome at Tulse Hill was pulled down

John Norman Lockyer, from a woodcut made about 1875.

(*Ronan Picture Library*)

The first visitation to Greenwich during Dyson's period as Astronomer Royal by the Board of Visitors. Included in the group are Lord Lister (fourth from left), Lord Rayleigh (sixth from left), then Glaisher, W. G. Adams, the fourth Earl of Rosse (who continued his father's interest in astronomy), Andrew Common, Sir William Huggins and Frank Dyson. Lister has his hand on a Borzoi owned by one of the Misses Airy.

(Ronan Picture Library)

and replaced by a larger one, and a double telescope was installed, with an 18-inch reflector on one side and a 15-inch refractor on the other.

Needless to say he lost little time in making good use of the new equipment, although it was rather too large to operate on his own. In due course Huggins obtained help—'I had the great happiness,' he wrote,[5] 'of having secured an able and enthusiastic assistant, by my marriage in 1875'—but in spite of his wry humour this was no purely business arrangement, and according to his wife, Margaret Montefiore, it was 'a romantic marriage of the Browning order, quite as ideally happy for thirty-five years'. Her assistance was never confined to drudgery, for even as a girl she had been interested in astronomy and observed with a telescope and a spectroscope that she had made herself, and she and her husband began a research partnership that was valuable enough to be recognized in the scientific world. They had no family and the only other member of their household was a mastiff which Huggins had acquired after his mother's death. He called the dog Kepler because he claimed that it possessed great mathematical abilities which he delighted in showing off to his friends. Huggins would show the dog a piece of cake, make him sit, and then proceed to ask him sums in arithmetic—for instance the square root of 16 or 9, or such a sum as $6 + 12 - 3$ divided by 5; the dog barked his answers which, as they always came out either to 3 or 4, no doubt produced a twinkle in his master's eye: 'prolonged calculations', Margaret Huggins later commented, 'rather fatigue him'. Kepler also showed a marked repugnance for butcher's shops, and always gave them a wide berth: when Huggins discovered that the dog's father and grandfather had displayed the same strange dislike he wrote to Charles Darwin, who was impressed enough to write a letter to the scientific periodical *Nature,* quoting it as a case of 'inherited antipathy'.

The William and Margaret Huggins team was certainly as devoted and virtually as productive as that of William Herschel and his sister Caroline; in the years that followed, the work at Tulse Hill gave rise to one important result after another, and in particular they set about some solar studies and pursued the problem of measuring star velocities. Huggins's solar work, like his stellar work, had started before his marriage and had resulted in a technique for using his spectroscope to observe solar prominences in daylight; this itself was an important development, for the glare of the Sun's disk normally makes it quite impossible to observe them at all and previously the only observations that could be made were during the time of total solar eclipse— in other words for only a minute or two at irregular intervals and on eclipse expeditions to frequently out of the way places. After his marriage Huggins tried to learn from his solution of the prominence problem in the hope that he could observe the solar and corona in daylight, an even more difficult task since the corona, a pearly coloured atmosphere that extends far out from the Sun, is dim even during a total eclipse, having a brightness never greater than half that of the full Moon. A series of fifty photographs achieved some success, but the scientific world was not fully convinced and the atmosphere at Tulse Hill was seldom clear enough for him to repeat his experiments.

Huggins's work on the corona was valiant though unsatisfactory, but there could be no criticism of the measurements he made of stellar velocities. Again this was pioneer work, which was to enlarge with one stroke the astronomer's knowledge about stellar motions, solving a problem which in earlier times had been intractable. That the stars move had been discovered by Halley and measurements of these motions had been made at Greenwich and elsewhere, but this was only half the problem: the measurements concerned motions across the sky but could not take account of motions the stars might possess directly towards the observer or away from him—'line of sight' velocities were undetectable by any known method using even the largest telescopes. The failure to detect such motions was due to the immense distance of the stars: in any telescope each appeared (and still appears) as no more than a pinpoint of light too small even to permit its diameter to be determined. In consequence the usual way of detecting an approach or a recession by a change of size could not be used; if stars were rushing towards or away from the observer they showed no direct evidence of the fact.

In 1842 Christian Doppler (1803–1853) in Prague had suggested a way out of this impasse by drawing an analogy between sound waves and light waves (a wave theory of light having become generally accepted some fifteen years earlier). Doppler argued that since the whistle of a railway train is higher in pitch when it is approaching an observer who is, say, standing on a station platform, and lower in pitch whilst it is moving away, there should be an analagous effect with starlight. The phenomenon of the train whistle, as Doppler readily appreciated, is caused by the frequency with which the sound waves reach the observer's ears : when the train approaches the waves follow one another more frequently because the distance they have to travel is constantly decreasing, and when the train is moving away the distance over which they have to travel is constantly increasing and the frequency with which they reach the ears is therefore reduced. Thus, since the pitch at which we hear a sound depends upon the frequency of the sound waves—the higher the pitch the higher the frequency—we shall perceive the approaching train by a high pitched whistle and the departing train by a whistle of lower pitch. As far as starlight is concerned, Doppler was of the opinion that the light waves would be increased in frequency from an approaching star, and appear bluer than usual, while from a star that was moving away, the light frequency would be lower and the star would have a reddish appearance.

The analogy was far from perfect however, and as the French physicist Hippolyte Fizeau (1819–1896) pointed out, was invalidated by the fact that the stars emit more radiation than the eye can perceive. As long ago as 1800 William Herschel had conducted his experiments proving that the Sun emitted heat infra-red rays (see p. 110) beyond the red end of the visible spectrum, while Johann Ritter had discovered ultra-violet rays that lay beyond the violet end. Fizeau made the obvious deduction that the change of colour which Doppler predicted would not occur, since the recession of a star would merely lower frequencies so that the ultra-violet light would appear as violet light and there would be an equivalent shift throughout the entire spectrum : the superficial appearance of the star would not alter at all. With an approaching star frequencies would be raised and rays that were originally infra-red would appear as red and, again, the general appearance of the star would remain the same. But Fizeau had an interest in spectroscopy and he therefore took his argument a stage further, pointing

179

out that although the superficial appearance of stars would remain unaltered by approach or recession, their spectra would show a change, which would manifest itself as a shift of the spectral lines. The shift would occur because each line is caused by light waves of a particular frequency, and if the apparent frequency changes so must the position in the spectrum at which the line appears. This, then, is what Huggins decided to try to observe.

The work was delicate since the line shifts to be observed were expected to be small, but early in 1868 he obtained his first result, detecting shift in the spectral lines from Sirius and proving that it was receding with a speed of twenty-nine and a half miles per second. After his marriage Huggins improved his equipment and in a paper written under the joint names of his wife and himself (as were all his future publications), he determined the line-of-sight velocities of thirty more stars. But the Hugginses' major achievements were their studies by photography of the invisible ultra-violet spectrum of Sirius— a set of observations that paved the way for further work along these lines in observatories all over the world—and their *Atlas of Stellar Spectra,* published in 1899. These, coupled with Huggins's previous work, brought public recognition including honorary degrees, a K.C.B., Presidency of the Royal Society and the receipt of one of the first Orders of Merit in 1902.

In 1908 Huggins found that he could observe no more, or rather that he was not able to prosecute his research with that vigour which made full scientific use of his elaborate equipment, and he asked the Royal Society to seee that it went to an institution that could carry on the work he had started. He himself suggested that it should all be removed to the Department of Astrophysics at Cambridge, the Society agreed, and Howard Grubb himself came over from Dublin to supervise the removal. Grubb's notes are worth recalling.[6] 'The Equatorial had been partially dismounted; all the numerous parts and attachments had been removed and were scattered over the floor, which was encumbered and littered with axes and various parts of the instrument, some of which had been already placed in packing cases; and in the midst of this litter, wrapped in a large cape and seated on a packing case, was Sir William himself, and his faithful collaboratrice who was flitting about watching the packing with keen interest and loving care. . . . Lady Huggins had asked me to let her know when I was ready to close the box [which contained the large object-glass from the telescope], and when I intimated that I had it safely in the case, she took Sir William by the hand and brought him across the room to have a last look at their very old friend. . . . They gazed long and sadly before I closed the lid.' Two years later Huggins died; although his stocky figure was sadly missed, the work he had initiated began to bear fruit wherever astronomy was studied.

Huggins had never been alone in his spectroscopic research and it was while he was still at the height of his powers that this kind of work was taken up at Greenwich, which, in 1881, had come under the leadership of a new Astronomer Royal, William Mahoney Christie (1845–1922). Christie had been Chief Assistant to Airy and had even then begun to develop a more purely scientific side to the observatory's work. In 1872, two years after his appointment as Chief Assistant, a programme involving the measurement of line-of-sight velocities was begun; and although this could be looked upon as yet another aspect of the observatory's duty to make precise measurements of the stars, it was the beginning of an era of pure research that has developed ever since. To begin with Airy had considered spectro-scopy as lying outside the observatory's scope, but the work of Huggins on velocity measurements assuaged his conscience, and with the 'great equatorial', which had a 12¾-inch object-glass, observations commenced. But as E. Walter Maunder, the assistant in charge of the observing programme with Christie, remarked :[7] the telescope 'was not powerful enough to do much more than afford a general indication of the direction in which the principal stars were moving, and to confirm in a general way the inference which various astronomers had found, from discussing the proper motions of the stars, that the sun and the solar system were moving towards that part of the heavens where the constellations Hercules and Lyra are placed.' In 1891 Christie had agreed that the programme could be taken no further with the refractor, and it was removed to make room for a much larger instrument of 26-inches aperture designed specifically for photographic work. This was donated by Sir Henry Thompson, a surgeon of substantial means who had already given the observatory a new photoheliograph. Thompson's magnificent gifts to Greenwich did not end with this refractor, for he also provided money for a 36-inch reflector.

Under Christie's administration the observatory buildings multiplied, and even the Admiralty were persuaded in 1886 to provide a 28-inch refractor: an instrument which could be used for what quite rightly was considered to be important research, the measurement of double stars, but which even in the wilder flights of fancy could not really be considered to lie within the terms of the observatory's original charter. Although the Admiralty gave no formal blessing to the increase in purely scientific pursuits, they no doubt realised that no institution like the Royal Observatory could possibly confine itself to utilitarian observations alone if it was to attract men with high qualifications and great ability: moreover there was the additional argument that a national observatory should undertake those aspects of long-term research that can rarely, if ever, be tackled at a university or private observatory. At any rate, whatever arguments Christie used, the Admiralty seemed to raise no objections and their liberal-minded attitude helped the observatory's development not a little.

Christie was a well-to-do man of some influence as well as outstanding ability. He had his own private yacht and was well connected at Court, was a personal friend of Edward VII, and used often to lunch with Queen Victoria; on one such occasion he had an experience which shows the Queen in a better light than she is sometimes presented. One of her granddaughters was there and when the Queen picked up a drumstick in her fingers and began to chew it, the granddaughter burst forth with 'Ooh, you dirty pig!' For a moment there was a shocked silence, Christie and fellow guests no doubt waiting with awe for the stern voice of royal disapproval, but Queen Victoria gently explained that she had been brought up by a German, and that in Germany such behaviour was no breach of good manners; but, she went on, the child's governess was quite right, eating with the hands was not good manners for the English.

When occasion demanded Christie could stand on his dignity and be very firm with the Admiralty. Extracts from a letter written towards the end of September 1910 in answer to official criticisms that some sections of his 1909 and 1910 Reports to the Board of Visitors were unsuitable for inclusion in the Observatory's annual report speak for themselves:[7] '... the statements for the years 1909/10 are in accordance with the practice... which has obtained upwards of seventy years.... Their Lordships appear to be under a misapprehension as to the position of the Astronomer Royal.... The Astronomer Royal is not appointed by the Board of Admiralty, but holds office directly from the Crown under a Royal Warrant.' He then goes on: 'As regards the presentation to Parliament of mutilated versions of my Report to the Board of Visitors for 1909 and 1910, I have the honour to state for the information of the Lords Commissioners of the Admiralty that the appending of my signature to these documents which purport to be the "Report of the Astronomer Royal to the Board of Visitors read at the Annual Visitation" has not been in any way authorised by me.'

Yet if Christie began the great transformation of the Royal Observatory into an institution for scientific research, he never neglected his more prosaic duties. Two years after his appointment as Astronomer Royal a conference was called in Washington by the State Department to see whether some final agreement could be reached over the choice of an internationally agreed prime meridian with a view to standardising the longitude figures on maps and navigators' charts. At this time the French used the meridian of Paris, the United States as well as Britain and its colonies used the meridian of Greenwich. At the conference it was decided by an overwhelming majority to use the Greenwich meridian: how much this was due to cogent argument and how much to Christie's tact will perhaps always remain unknown, but the decision once again echoed the reputation of the Royal Observatory.

It was at this conference that the concomitant problem of dividing the world into standard time zones was also discussed, a problem which was assuming increasing importance in large countries like the United States where quick travel by railway was liable to cause chaos if different times were used at different places, and even in Britain the question had already raised legal and othe issues. The mean solar time of the astronomer was originally adopted for clocks, but even so there was a local rule that noon at any place was the time when the Sun

183

was on the meridian: according to this reckoning noon in Cornwall occurred twenty minutes later than in London, an arrangement that could, and did, cause immense problems in compiling intelligible railway timetables, and in 1858 was responsible for a legal conundrum. In this year a case was heard in Carlisle without the defendant present, as the Court sat according to Greenwich time while the defendant appeared later, having relied on local time: he had been tried in his absence and found guilty. A new trial was ordered, but there was clearly a need for appropriate legislation, and finally in 1880 a 'Definition of Time' statute was enacted which at last made Greenwich Mean Time—or 'railway time' as it was called for many years—the official time of the country; Ireland followed suit in 1916. The problem of time zones was merely an extension of this scheme on a world-wide basis and this the conference hammered out, deciding to divide the world into twenty-four zones, each differing from the next by one hour and each extending over fifteen degrees of longitude: it was a wise and workable solution which is still relevant even today when fast travel by jet aircraft is the rule.

Christie's direction of the Royal Observatory was carried out with a tact and humour that endeared him to his staff. He used to amuse himself on occasions by pointing out to the enquirers who asked him to cast their horoscopes that he was Astronomer not Astrologer Royal, and he took a lively interest in popularising astronomy, being the founder of *The Observatory,* an astronomical magazine whose contents were rather less austere than those of the journals of learned societies. Furthermore, excitements at the Royal Observatory were not confined to those moments of successful research or battles with the Board of Admiralty: in 1894 there was an attack by anarchists, one of whom mutilated himself beyond repair when his home-made bomb exploded prematurely on the meridian line. But the eighth Astronomer Royal must be remembered above all for his expansion of the Royal Observatory in both its main roles as a time-honoured centre for precise measurement, and as a leading institution for research—in days when British astronomy was forging ahead into new and promising fields.

IX

Theories of the Universe

THE LATE NINETEENTH CENTURY and the first sixty
years of the twentieth have shown a revival of interest in a
problem which had intrigued the Greeks and various astronomers
off and on ever since—the nature of the universe. The Greeks
had used both logic and imagination as tools in their speculations, but their primary guide had been aesthetic suitability;
Thomas Digges, Thomas Wright and William Herschel had
used imagination coupled with observation—producing in Herschel's case the most careful and painstaking survey that had
ever been made of stellar distribution. The philosopher Immanuel
Kant and the mathematician Pierre Laplace had discussed the
possible origin of the solar system from a rotating mass of
gas which condensed into separate planetary bodies: but now,
with the advent of spectroscopy, and the power to measure
stellar distance, to detect stellar motions, and to differentiate
between at least two kinds of nebulae, a crop of new observa-
ional evidence was to hand. The astronomer could speculate
with a hard core of scientific facts to keep his feet firmly on
the ground, and he was not slow to take advantage of the new
situation.

It was a civil servant who first brought forward a novel
hypothesis, an amateur astronomer whose duties were to edit
Army Regulations, but whose heart lay elsewhere. J. Norman
Lockyer (1836–1920), began his astronomical work with good
equipment, a 6¼-inch refractor by Thomas Cooke of York, and
to start with concentrated his attention on the planets, particularly Mars. But when Kirchhoff and Bunsen reached their
penetrating conclusions about the spectrum, Lockyer, like
Huggins, began to turn his attention to this new and exciting

185

field: however, instead of trying to examine the spectra of stars, he decided to concentrate his attentions on the Sun. By 1866 he had done enough to prove that sunspots appeared dark against the bright disk of the Sun not only because of the feebleness of their light—the generally accepted view—but also because they absorbed a far greater amount of sunlight than their surroundings; and it was he who in 1868 at the same time as Pierre Janssen, discovered that the prominences could be observed in daylight and without an eclipse by widening the narrow slit of the spectroscope: a fact also hit upon by Huggins a little later, and put to use by astronomers everywhere.

Lockyer was enthusiastic enough not to rest here and he became a leading figure in solar research, charting the movements of prominences, classifying them and, in 1866, producing a theory about the cause of sunspots which, although it is ruled out of court today, proved its worth at the time in provoking some disagreement and a considerable amount of further research. Although still officially at the War Office, Lockyer took on the editorship of *Nature* as a spare-time job and a year later, in 1870, became secretary to a Royal Commission on Scientific Instruction and the Advancement of Science: a post that was to prove a turning point in his career. The Commission took six years over its deliberations, but when its conclusions were announced they included a proposal that a solar observatory for the express purpose of studying solar physics should be established at the Science and Art Department* at South Kensington, and Lockyer was transferred from the War Office to take command; later he became lecturer at the Royal College of Science and, in 1887, professor of astronomical physics. Many astronomers helped in the formation of the solar observatory, not least William Christie, and with Lockyer in charge it soon began to make its presence known with the careful spectrocopic observations that were made and the extension of the work into the realm of stellar spectra. Lockyer's work continued until his death, even though he was forced to retire in 1901 and the observatory at South Kensington was dismantled in 1913 and packed off to Cambridge: by then in his late seventies, Lockyer merely moved to Sidmouth and started a new observatory.

* Later to become the Imperial College of London University.

Lockyer's two adventures into the theoretical side of astronomy, however, are what most concern us; his first theory suggested the gradual evolution of stars and his second concerned the formation of the planets. The first of these, the evolution of stars, arose from the new outlook of astronomers, and came into astronomy, and many other sciences, initiated by the publication in 1859 of Charles Darwin's *Origin of Species*. The concept gained ground that gradual large-scale change was a characteristic of the universe, and although there may be philosophical reasons why the 'evolution' of stars might better be called their 'life history', the term evolution has remained and is still common currency. Lockyer suggested that stars changed in temperature as they aged, beginning as cool, comparatively dim bodies, developing into hot bright spheres of gas, and finally ending their days as cooler and dimmer objects once again. It was an ingenious interpretation of the evidence he could extract from an analysis and classification of spectra; but it was at variance with another equally ingenious and, on the face of it, more plausible hypothesis proposed in 1913 by Henry Norris Russell and Ejnar Hertzsprung in Princeton: they believed that the evidence led to the supposition that all stars began as hot bright bodies and gradually, through loss of heat, became cooler and dimmer. In the days before there was any corpus of knowledge either of the internal constitution of stars or of their method of heat generation, the Hertzsprung-Russell hypothesis seemed the more likely, and was for years the generally accepted explanation: only now, in the nineteen sixties, are the tables being turned and the development of stars from cool to hot is becoming the accepted theory, at least as far as the majority of astronomers are concerned.

Lockyer's other, and at the time more acceptable, theory was his 1890 'meteoric hypothesis'. Astronomers in the nineteenth century had taken a considerable step forward when they discovered a vital link between comets and meteors, for it was then realised that meteors, and particularly those that arrived in showers at various months in the year, were the debris of comets, the jetsam strewn out along a cometary orbit as the comet itself came close to the Sun and began a species of disintegration. The significance for Lockyer of this correlation was that it indicated the likelihood of there being a considerable amount of meteoric material in the solar system, and from this, the probability that in the past there was more meteoric material still, since every time a meteor falls into a planetary atmosphere, it becomes wasted away by atmospheric friction. Lockyer therefore based his theory on the assumption of the ubiquity of meteoric material throughout the entire universe, with the corollary that 'all self-luminous bodies in the celestial space are composed either of swarms of meteorites, or of masses of meteoric vapour produced by heat'.[1] With this in mind, he was led to his stellar evolutionary sequence which moved from nebulae and very gaseous stars, producing spectra with bright lines so characteristic of laboratory gases, up through red coolish stars, to stars not very dissimilar to the Sun, with hot bright stars typified by Sirius at the peak. From here his hierarchy descended through stars precisely like the Sun down to cooler bodies and thence to death as cold condensed objects, no longer shining by their own light. The idea of a continuous growth from an original mass of material was a bold and imaginative stroke, and if modern nuclear physics has made this untenable, that does not detract from its value as a stimulant, important at the time since Lockyer also coupled it with his 'dissociation hypothesis'. This was a theory far ahead of its time in explaining the different kinds of stellar spectra by the supposition that all atoms of whatever substance they might be, were in essence merely different groupings of the self-same atomic 'bits and pieces'—a theory that in fact postulated the existence of particles smaller than atoms, and this more than two decades before laboratory experiments led physicists to the same conclusion.

Astronomical spectroscopy was proving its worth and it is no wonder that it was pursued with immense vigour in every large observatory. At the Royal Observatory at Edinburgh, stellar spectra were an important part of the observing programme, and at Cambridge the director Hugh Newall, using a large 25-inch refractor donated by his father, followed up Huggins' work and expanded this side of the observatory's activities when Huggins' own equipment arrived from Tulse Hill. But observations alone were not enough, and it was fortunate that in the early years of the present century Britain possessed two active and penetrating theoreticians who, in spite of their disagreement—or perhaps because of it—contributed much to theories of the constitution of the stars and the evolution of the universe.

The first of these, James Jeans (1877–1946), is now best remembered for a series of nine popular books on astronomy and physics which received a circulation to be envied by a best-selling novelist, but he was trained as a mathematician and was a university lecturer on the subject at Cambridge before he was thirty. Jeans was incidentally a good and enthusiastic musician, a director of the Royal Academy of Music, and towards the end of his life devoted more time to music than to astronomy—a mirror image, as it were, of William Herschel. His early research was concerned with the problems of bodies in motion, but it was not long before he turned his attention to the motions of stars and the behaviour of the gases of which they are composed. From this work he computed the age of the universe: first analysing the likely ages of stars, which he found to be millions upon millions of years, and then working out how long the present situation would have taken to arise, assuming that clusters of stars and binary stars (then recognised in their thousands by astronomers) had evolved gradually. The mechanism for forming clusters of binaries which Jeans took as his foundation was based on the well accepted facts of universal gravitation and led him, in the end, to support the view that the universe was very old—some five million million years at the least. This seemed to fit in well with what was then known about the age of the Earth, which must, astronomers agreed, be younger than the universe in which it was situated; the creation account in the first chapter of Genesis no longer made for difficulties since its literal interpretation had long been questioned. However, Jeans's ideas were not accepted without argument. His chief antagonist was Arthur Eddington (1882–1944), who was his equal as a mathematician and had for a time been a Chief Assistant at Greenwich before taking the Plumian professorship of astronomy and experimental philosophy at Cambridge.

Eddington had already achieved a considerable reputation as a cosmologist, since it was he who introduced into Britain the theory of relativity that Albert Einstein had propounded in a series of scientific papers between 1905 and 1915.* This had demanded a great advocacy, since relativity theory, to some scientists at least, appeared to be full of concepts too revolutionary to be taken as more than a mathematical fiction: indeed even Eddington himself had been forced to admit that 'Whether the theory ultimately proves to be correct or not, it claims attention as being one of the most beautiful examples of the power of general mathematical reasoning'.[2] Eddington had been impressed by the anomaly in the motion of Mercury's orbit for which Newtonian gravitation had been unable to account, but for which relativity theory offered an explanation, and it was he who in 1919, conducted an expedition to Principe, an island off the coast of Spanish Guinea, to observe a total solar eclipse with a view to obtaining confirmation. One consequence of Einstein's theory was that beams of light must be deflected by gravitation, and Eddington's scheme was to photograph the stars that were visible in the darkened sky during the period of totality and then compare their positions with photographs taken on an ordinary night at some other time without the Sun in close proximity. If Einstein were correct, the apparent positions of the stars ought to be closer to the Sun during the eclipse, as their light would be deflected out of its path by the Sun's strong gravitational pull.

The expedition took some time: Eddington and his assistant sailed in March, but it was not until mid-May that they were settled and Eddington had his standard photographs of the relevant field of stars. The eclipse was due on 29 May at about two in the afternoon, and in the morning there was, in Eddington's words, 'a tremendous rainstorm'. However, he goes on,[3] 'The rain stopped about noon and about 1.30 ... we began to get a glimpse of the sun. We had to carry out our photographs in faith. I did not see the eclipse, being too busy changing plates, except for one glance to make sure that it had begun and another half-way through to see how much cloud there was. We took sixteen photographs. They are all good of the sun, showing a very remarkable prominence; but the cloud has interfered with the star images. The last few

* No attempt will be made here to discuss relativity theory, but the reader is referred, for instance, to William Bonner's *The Mystery of the Expanding Universe*, Eyre & Spottiswoode, London, 1964.

photographs show a few images which I hope will give us what we need. . . .' The photographs were developed then and there on Principe, but the cloudy weather had made for difficulties and it took Eddington longer than he had intended to measure and calculate. But on 3 June he was able to enter triumphantly in his notebook, '. . . the one plate I measured gave a result agreeing with Einstein'. Another Greenwich expedition to Sobral in Brazil had better weather and their photographs, when measured, confirmed Eddington's. How important these results were, he summed up in a parody of the Rubáiyát, his closing stanza of which ran: [4]

'Oh leave the Wise our measures to collate
One thing at least is certain, LIGHT has weight
One thing is certain and the rest debate—
Light-rays, when near the Sun, DO NOT GO STRAIGHT.'

But even with the movement of Mercury and the evidence of the 1919 eclipse that light was attracted by gravity and so, as Eddington parodied, possessed weight, relativity was still not out of the wood—one crucial test remained, one final trial which if it came to nothing would bring the whole elaborate structure tumbling down about Eddington's and Einstein's ears. This was the prediction that since light was attracted by gravitation, the light waves emitted from a large body such as a star would be slightly attracted by its *own* gravitation and appear to be reduced in frequency—in other words, there ought to be a permanent red shift of the lines of, say, the solar spectrum. Calculation showed that the shift was small, and its detection presented technical problems to the astronomical physicist. John Evershed (1864–1956), a careful and accurate observer and expert in solar physics, working at the British observatory in Kodiakanal near Madras, had by 1921 convinced himself that the shift was discernible; but it was very difficult to separate it from the shifts due to rotation of the Sun, movement of the Earth, and the actual movements of gases close to the solar surface, and the world remained unconvinced. At Mount Wilson Observatory in California, with its elaborate equipment designed specifically to study the solar spectrum, observers were less certain than Evershed and it was not until 1923 that a shift very close to that computed by Einstein was observed. Even so a special allowance had to be made for gas motion within the Sun to obtain agreement with Einstein's figures, and it is only fair to say that full confirmation is still awaited at the present time. On the other hand the nearness of the Mount Wilson figure and the concordance of Mercury's motion, the results of the two Greenwich eclipse expeditions and the confirmation of their observations by a United States team and another from Greenwich at the total solar eclipse of 1922, were sufficient to demolish the critics.

The importance of relativity is that it not only affects astronomy and the whole of the astronomer's concept of the entire universe, giving a broader and more extensive grasp of phenomena than was possible with Newtonian gravitation, but that it also has ramifications running through the whole of atomic physics. The energy released in a nuclear bomb can be computed on relativity theory, but lies outside the boundaries of Newtonian physics; Newton, however, is not 'wrong', but rather more limited in approach to the vast problem of the whole of physical creation.

Relativity also takes in its stride a new discovery about the cosmos that all cosmologists take into account today, the strange fact that the entire universe appears to be expanding. This idea has arisen from observational evidence on the galaxies: once Rosse and others had discovered that some 'nebulae' were spiral in structure and Huggins had found that the spirals gave the spectra of conglomerations of stars rather than clouds of gas, it gradually became clear, after the giant 100-inch reflector at Mount Wilson had been at work for a few years, that the construction of the universe was grander in scale than even Herschel or Wright had imagined. The Sun, it was found, was one of thousands of millions of stars making up not the cosmos, but one spiral galaxy within it. Outside this galaxy were thousands, nay millions, of others: the universe was a universe of star islands stretching out as far as the photographic plate could reach. With the development of photographic and spectroscopic techniques another factor had been found to operate both close to and away in the furthest reaches of space, the factor of expansion. Every spiral galaxy possessed a red shift of its spectral lines, in every case the lines were displaced from their 'true' laboratory position and moved by a greater or lesser degree towards the red end of the spectrum; this shift, accord-

The movable aerial (on raised rails) of Sir Martin Ryle's first large aperture synthesis radio telescope at the Mullard Radio Astronomy Observatory at Cambridge.

(*Ronan Picture Library*)

The control panel and Sir Bernard Lovell's Mark I (250 foot diameter) radio telescope at Jodrell Bank.

(Ronan Picture Library)

ing to the Doppler-Fizeau interpretation, means only one thing: that galaxies were all moving away from us—and, on further analysis, that they moved away with a velocity that depended on their distance, those further away receding more quickly than those closer to. It was indeed just as if a bomb had exploded and the galaxies were the shrapnel moving outwards; the 'expanding universe', as Eddington called it, was the new and phenomenal picture that astronomy presented. On Einstein's relativity theory an expanding universe was one of the possibilities, and this again appeared not so much to support but rather to underline the validity of this novel synthesis of physical knowledge.

The broad sweep of a theory is all very well—it provides a way of glimpsing the grand pageant of the heavens and correlating all the diverse aspects of it with which astronomers have to deal; but although the cosmologist has the entire universe as his canvas, he must not and cannot neglect the details. It is from small inconsistencies that old theories die and new ones are born. Eddington, and Jeans for that matter, never forgot those details and their battles over the structure of stars—a more 'homely' subject than relativity, Eddington called it—was a noble and fruitful one. The basic problems that faced them were to try to determine what the internal conditions of stars are like, what causes them to shine as they do mainly in this colour or that, what makes some hotter than others, and a host of similar questions that can all be grouped under the umbrella of stellar physics.

The problems are technical and complex, but in essence Eddington believed that all the evidence pointed to stars being bodies of great age, measured in millions of years, and in consequence to their possessing some way of generating energy that was then unknown. As he surmised, 'probably the simplest hypothesis . . . is that there may be a slow process of annihilation of matter':[5] in other words that matter was being transformed into energy at the atomic level, as relativity theory indicated was quite possible, and this would naturally enough provide an almost inexhaustible store of energy. Eddington also believed that stars were far from remaining in a steady state—most probably they would grow fatter or leaner depending on the rate at which their energy was being generated at the time,

N

and on occasions they might even be disrupted. Jeans, on the other hand, considered that stars remained far more steady than Eddington was willing to concede and, what is more, he seemed to look with suspicion on the idea that matter was being annihilated deep within them. Jeans felt it more likely that most, if not all stars, derived at least the major part of their energy by contracting as they aged, since, if a gaseous body contracts then its central temperature rises and, in such a way, a star will be able to maintain its brightness for a very long time. Moreover there are problems in connection with the way radiation escapes from stellar interiors, for since the bodies are composed of dense gas, light and radiant heat cannot readily flow away and some explanation to account for the transference of radiation from inside to outside is a vital part of any stellar hypothesis. Here again Jeans and Eddington did not very often see eye to eye and their arguments became a regular feature at meetings of the Royal Astronomical Society in the year 1917 to the mid-1920's.

Jeans's long time-scale of the universe has now become unfashionable and unlikely, and it is generally agreed that in his battles with Eddington he never won the final victory; but the arguments and the discussions, including the very real contribution Jeans made towards understanding the transference of stellar radiation, all cleared the ground and laid foundations on which others could build. At Cambridge the university observatory was committed to a programme of spectroscopic research under Professor Frederick Stratton (1881–1960); at Oxford university observatory spectroscopy was part of the research effort; and at St Andrews, Edinburgh, and Greenwich the spectroscope was in continual use. But in spite of all this effort, the internal constitution of the stars still remained a mystery, although Jeans and Eddington between them had sorted out a great deal of the problem.

Eddington's belief that the annihilation of matter was the source of stellar energy, that the breakdown of atoms within the dense central parts of a star was the cause of its immense supplies of radiation, received support in 1932 when Robert d'Escourt Atkinson of the Royal Observatory at Greenwich worked out the quantity of energy that would be released inside a stellar interior and, more important still, the precise sub-atomic process that could be involved. Thus, before the generation of energy by the breakdown of atoms and the release and collision of the even smaller particles of which they were composed had been transformed from a theoretical dream into a dreadful reality at Hiroshima, Atkinson was working out the details in an astronomical context. This was doubly significant: not only did it provide an underlying cause for the general pattern of relationships among the spectra of the majority of stars, but it also supported Eddington's feeling that the very long time-scale for the universe was invalid. It seemed possible now that the age was more likely to be measured in thousands of millions of years rather than millions of millions. But more work and more knowledge about the transformation of atoms into energy was required before a decision could be made or even before Atkinson's ideas could be carried much further, and this took time—so much time that substantial advances had to wait until after the Second World War.

Eddington, hard-headed mathematician and down-to-earth astronomer though he might be, possessed a mystical side to his nature and the last years of his life were spent in an attempt to construct a huge relativistic synthesis of the physical universe, an edifice in which the bricks would be the sub-atomic and astronomical evidence of the observer and the mortar the underlying mathematical relationships between them. The whole scheme, which Eddington called his Fundamental Theory, was a complex of ideas which even led him to a computation involving the total number of basic atomic particles in the universe. But the theory was never finished, as Eddington died while he was still at work on it, and although the results he had obtained were published posthumously,* its implications have not yet been fully fathomed. One is here reminded a little of John Dee, who also sought mystical yet natural relationships between diverse aspects of the universe as he understood it, and a temptation arises to look on Eddington as the modern equivalent of a hermetist with a hierarchy of matter to replace the hierarchy of angels and archangels in which Dee believed. But this temptation to compare the two, to see in Eddington a similar underlying motive to that which possessed the sixteenth-century hermetist, must not be pressed too far.

* A. S. Eddington, *Fundamental Theory*, Cambridge, 1946.

Eddington used the hard facts of observation, the evidence of others besides himself, and in this sense at least his construction was built on a foundation that was undeniably solid: his mysticism was tempered at every turn by common scientific experience.

Theories of the universe which could take into account its expansion—a factor that Eddington believed made a 'short' time-scale imperative and which he had expressed in his wonderfully written popular expositions as well as in his scientific papers —came from many quarters after the publication of Einstein's relativity theory. All were necessarily mathematical, as relativity itself is essentially a theory of mathematical physics, and in Britain such a theory which provided a compromise between the long and short time-scales was proposed in 1933 by Edward Milne (1896–1950). Known as 'kinematical relativity', it suggested that there were two different time-scales in the universe: the scale by which we live and on which the scientist bases his meaurements, and another which is far more basic, more fundamental, and the one that governs all sub-atomic processes. On the everyday scale the age of the universe worked out to about two thousand million years, supporting Eddington's view, but on the atomic time-scale the age had no limit: one figure gave a short time-scale and the other a scale that was infinitely long. Milne's result, published in 1935, convinced neither Eddington nor Jeans, but its ingenuity was plain and kinematical relativity proved to be an interesting step on the way to a more comprehensive picture of the cosmos. Yet it underlined more or less emphatically the need for more facts and deeper knowledge of the physical processes involved both inside stars and galaxies, and within the atoms that composed them. This was to lie some two decades in the future.

But if theories of cosmology, arguments about the time-scale of the universe, and studies of the internal constitution of the stars occupied the thoughts and energies of many astronomers, there was still no cessation in the prosecution of accurate measurement and the determination of those details without which theories, be they ever so ingenious, are a mere beating of the air. In this Greenwich, as always, led the field. Christie had retired in 1910 but his expansive approach continued under his successor Frank Dyson, who was the driving force behind the plan to send the eclipse expeditions to Principe and Sobral in 1919 as soon as the Armistice had been signed and transport was certain. Dyson was well aware of the importance Eddington attached to the observations and is said to have remarked to Cottingham, Eddington's assistant, during their briefing session that if the shift of the stars did not come out to the value calculated from Einstein's theory, Eddington would go mad and the assistant would have to come home alone; when Eddington had developed and measured a plate on Principe and found that the theory and observation coincided, he turned to his companion and said,[6] 'Cottingham, you won't have to go home alone.'

It was during Dyson's direction of Greenwich that the problem of time determination took a great stride forward. When he took over from Christie the standard timepieces of the observatory were no longer the simple electric clocks installed by Airy but electric pendulum clocks of far greater accuracy. This improvement arose because their pendulums swung in a chamber where air pressure was constant and the temperature controlled within close limits and the pendulum itself was thus almost 'free', having little work to do other than to make and break an electric circuit. Such 'freedom' was vital, since a pendulum is essentially a regulator and its time-keeping ability depends on its being left alone so that it may swing at its natural period—a 'seconds' pendulum if left to itself will, provided it is kept at a constant temperature and pressure, swing with a total side-to-side motion that takes neither more nor less than two seconds. Difficulties arise as soon as the pendulum is used in a clock: the pendulum must continually receive small impulses if it is to keep going without cessation, and it must give up some of its energy from time to time if it is to operate a clock dial or even to open and close electric contacts permitting other machinery to do the necessary work of moving the hands.

In the late nineteenth century the German instrument maker Riefler had gone some way to achieve this ideal, paying particular attention to the instant at which the pendulum received the periodic impulse that kept it going, so that the pendulum's freedom was interfered with as little as possible, and the error of his clocks was of the order of no more than about one hundredth of a second per day. Surprisingly enough this accuracy was not sufficient, for by the early years of this century new developments in laboratory physics and in the growing fields of radio and electronics made it desirable if not imperative to have clocks that did better than this. The necessity for what appears on the surface to be a quite unnecessary degree of precision arose from the need to measure accurately very small fractions of a second: a simple calculation shows that this, in turn, demands a daily error in a clock of nowhere near as high as one hundredth of a second. For suppose we need to able to determine the duration of something in the laboratory which occurs for no more than one millionth of a second (and such small intervals are needed in radio work): this means that time measurement must be correct to one part in ten million. In one day (twenty-four hours) there are 86,000 seconds and a clock with an error of no more than one hundredth of a second in this time is not correct to one part in ten million, but rather less. The demand for timekeeping with what may seem an inordinate amount of precision is therefore in no way unreasonable.

Riefler's clocks, good though they were, had not a sufficient degree of accuracy, but the problem of attaining anything much better meant a reappraisal of the errors forced on the swing of a pendulum by the impulses it received and the work it had to do: and for some time, the further the matter was investigated the less did it seem possible to achieve a substantial improvement. A solution was found in the end, however, and not by an astronomer but by a civil engineer, W. H. Shortt (? –1928). In every clock Shortt used two pendulums, one to do the work—the 'slave' as he called it—and one to do nothing but swing—the 'free' pendulum. At least this was the basis of the ingenious idea, but as may be imagined it was rather more complex in practice and is worth looking into rather more fully. The free pendulum, which was the crux of the invention, was a normal pendulum designed to operate in a temperature and pressure controlled chamber and to receive its impulse only once every half-minute, quite sufficient to maintain its regular swing. The method of providing this impulse was, however, extraordinary clever, for Shortt arranged that it should be controlled by the slave pendulum and the push given by a small electrically operated arm or pallet that fell on to a protruding bar on the side of the free penduum. If the impulse appeared slightly early or slightly late—as it might well do considering that the slave pendulum was liable to errors caused by the various pieces of mechanism that it had to operate—then the length of time that the pallet lay next to the free pendulum would be different. This difference, which was an automatic measure of the error in the slave pendulum, was fed back to a second pallet that provided the slave with its impulse and gave a longer or shorter impulse as the case might be. In other words the free pendulum corrected the errors in the slave and was designed to do so through the impulse it received—it had to do no work, to operate no other mechanism, in order to achieve this. The correction was fed back by the efforts of the slave which provided the impulse in the first place, and although it seems rather a case of getting something for nothing, the device worked and, incidentally, worked very well.

Shortt was fortunate in having his invention taken up by the Synchronome Company, which was already manufacturing single pendulum clocks more than precise enough for everyday purposes, and the Shortt-Synchronome free pendulum was soon available to astronomers. Models were installed at both Edinburgh and Greenwich in 1924 and their accuracy surpassed the most sanguine hopes, giving time with an error that amounted to three or four times less than the Reifler clocks. At Greenwich the new clocks were placed in the old stone cellar of Flamsteed house and a constant stream of privileged visitors came to see them; the experts discussed the niceties of their design with Dyson, while others had to content themselves with his simple explanation that 'though the slave does most of the work, he has the pleasure of giving his master an occasional kick'.

Not long after the installation of the Shortt clocks, John Reith, director of the British Broadcasting Company, visited Dyson to discuss the possibility of broadcasting time signals from the observatory and explained how this service would enhance Greenwich's reputation. Dyson was indignant about the question of reputation—it rested, he was at pains to explain, on a sound scientific record—but he was interested in extending the time service by every possible means and was quite ready to discover how this could be done. Only a small sum was needed to modify two of the observatory's older electric clocks (made by Dent) so that they were controlled by the free pendulum and fitted with the necessary circuits to transmit six one-second pips into the broadcasting system. Three years later the time service was further extended by sending signals to the Post Office radio station at Rugby; from there they were transmitted on a wavelength that was convenient for world coverage and suitable for all ships at sea. The signals were more elaborate than those for domestic use and lasted for five minutes twice a day, thus allowing a navigator to determine the precise errors of his ship's chronometer merely by checking the broadcast signals against the audible ticks of the chronometer itself. With this new service, inaugurated two and a half centuries after the Royal Observatory had been founded, the old method of determining longitude by lunar distances at last became obsolete—technical advances had been made that even Maskelyne could not have gainsaid.

But if the time services of the observatory were improved by Dyson, there were other developments in the 1920's that boded ill for the future. In 1923 the suburban sections of the Southern Railway were electrified, and immediately the magnetic observations began to suffer: there was nothing for it but to remove the magnetic equipment to a new site, right away from artificial disturbance. Land was purchased at Abinger in Surrey, on the northern slope of Leith Hill, and a small magnetic observatory was erected; for many years all was well, especially since the opportunity was taken to provide new equipment technically superior to that previously employed. But if Abinger was suitably isolated from magnetic disturbance in 1923, it was not to be so for long: electrification of the Southern Railway moved further and further out from London and twenty years later Spencer Jones, Dyson's successor, was talking of yet another move, this time to some position remote from any likely ramifications of the railway network. As it turned out, the growth of London was to force the whole observatory to forsake its ancient home in 1948, but this was a move that Dyson did not live to see.

Dyson's reign at Greenwich was a fruitful one, in which staff relationships remained at the high standard they had reached in Christie's time. It was still possible for a young man

200

to join the staff in a junior capacity and, by dint of hard work, reach a position of real responsibility; this had happened most notably in Christie's day in the case of Philibert Melotte (1880–1961), who had joined the staff at fifteen as a young computer at a time when the *Carte du Ciel* project was under way, and became such an expert in celestial photography that he was able to photograph an object close to Jupiter which proved to be yet another satellite with a brightness some ten million times less than the planet itself. Melotte's was not the only such case in the annals, for there were examples in Dyson's time also. It was in Dyson's period, too, that the observatory held its 250th anniversary and received its first royal visit since the time of Queen Anne, when in July 1925 George V and Queen Mary spent an afternoon there—an event which aroused popular interest and focused attention both on the work at Greenwich and on Dyson himself. But doubtless the greatest recognition of his abilities came in 1936 when William Yapp, a wealthy manufacturer, followed the Thompson tradition and presented a large new telescope to the observatory. Yapp had visited Greenwich in 1928, as a guest of a member of the British Astronomical Association; this was a society primarily of amateur observers that had been formed in 1890, with men like Huggins among its early members, and it had close associations with Greenwich. Yapp seems to have been so impressed both by his reception and by what he saw that he insisted his gift should not go (as Dyson had generously suggested) to the Radcliffe Observatory established in Pretoria some time previously. Yapp wanted it to commemorate Dyson's directorship and donated a sum of £15,000. This was spent on a 36-inch reflector, which was brought into commission for spectroscopic work in 1934, the year after Dyson retired.

In spite of the difficulties that the continual enlargement of London had brought about—in nearby Greenwich an electric power station, built over disused horse-tram stables, was directly on the meridian line, with the result that representations had to be made to have two of its tall chimneys cut down—and after Dyson Spencer Jones (1890-1960) continued to expand and consolidate the work. Dyson had made a strong case for replacing the Airy transit circle and in 1936 the new circle was ready; but Spencer Jones was wondering how long the observatory could continue to function and to carry out its important work, as some activities were being increasingly hampered by the bright lights and haze from the nearby city. But the observatory's time department was one that was not adversely affected, and in this Spencer Jones took a special interest. He was an astronomer whose delight was to deal with methods of precision and he was always ready to welcome innovation whenever this could improve accuracy. By the time he assumed office in 1933 electronics were developing fast, and one of the more immediate effects was the invention of a completely novel method of timekeeping that obviated the need for a pendulum, free or otherwise. The heart of the new device was a crystal of quartz, a naturally occurring mineral that exhibits a piezo-electric (pressure-electric) effect: it distorts when a variable electric current is applied to two metal inserts or electrodes fitted into it. Conversely, if such a crystal is distorted either by the application of a varying electric current or by some physical pressure, the crystal generates a varying electric current of its own.

Crystals of this kind—and there are other besides quartz—are now used for many purposes—for example, as a way of controlling the frequency of the radio waves broadcast by a radio station—and it is the latter application that is the closest analogy to the quartz clock. The clock consists of a small kind of radio transmitter or oscillator that does no broadcasting out into space but passes its output down a wire in the form of a continuous flow of electric current, varying at a high frequency. This high frequency current is fed to the crystal, which goes into a state of oscillation on its own account and, because of its piezo-electric properties, emits its own high-frequency current: this current is fed back to the oscillator and is made to alter the high frequency emitted until this coincides with the high frequency of the crystal. The current is then as large as it can become and the device remains stable. With a crystal kept at a constant temperature and pressure—conditions not difficult to arrange for a device that is only about an inch across and can readily be sealed in an evacuated glass tube—the stability of the frequency is phenomenal, for it can remain correct to one part in one hundred thousand million, a degree of precision that cannot be approached (let alone equalled) by any mechanical device. As soon, then, as the quartz clock was out of the experimental stage, a number were installed at Greenwich and at Edinburgh, and the results were encouraging to say the least. Soon after this, in 1936, the 'talking clock' service was instituted for telephone subscribers so that Greenwich precision might be continuously available to all who required it.

The new clocks still needed to be checked with astronomical observations, and although Spencer Jones wanted a vertical telescope constructed for this purpose, as it happened such an instrument—a modern photographic version of Bradley's original zenith sector—was not forthcoming until after the Second World War. Meanwhile Spencer Jones devoted some of his efforts to a careful examination of time as determined by clocks and by star transits and in 1939 produced an analysis that caused no little stir. He proved conclusively that the rotating Earth, the basic timekeeper used by man from time immemorial, did not rotate regularly, and went on to show that these 'errors' in the Earth's rotation were the cause of apparent but unreal accelerations in the orbital motions of the Moon, the planets and the Earth itself: with one blow he used the latest and most precise measurements possible to clear up a problem of gravitational astronomy that had long puzzled astronomers.*

Spencer Jones took a great interest in the measurement of the Sun's distance and made some notable contributions to the problem, particularly when there was a very close approach of the minor planet Eros in 1930–31, just before he was appointed Astronomer Royal. Preparations were laid well beforehand and an international committee with Spencer Jones at its head planned a vast programme of photographic observations involving eighteen observatories in the northern hemisphere and six in the southern. So large a co-operative effort produced an immense amount of material totalling well over 2,800 photographic plates; it was at Greenwich that these were examined and analysed by Spencer Jones and Melotte for the next ten years and it was not until 1941 that the results and conclusions could be published, giving the distance of the Sun correct to within about ten thousand miles, or an error of no more than one part in nine thousand. This was the most correct figure in

* H. Spencer Jones, *Memoirs of the Royal Astronomical Society*, 66 (1941).

its day and represents the acme of determinations made by simultaneous optical observations from a number of stations.

The predilection for precise measurement did not lead to any slackening in the observatory's research programme, and the 36-inch Yapp reflector which Spencer Jones saw installed was immediately put to very good use by William Greaves (1897–1955), one of his Chief Assistants (the Admiralty having been persuaded by Dyson to permit the employment of more than one Assistant in view of the observatory's increased work). With the Yapp telescope, and later, on his appointment in 1938 to Edinburgh as Astronomer Royal for Scotland, with another 36-inch telescope, Greaves carried out an intense programme of spectrophotometry with a view to determining the temperatures of different types of star. Essentially this work consists in photographing the spectra of stars in a standard way and then carrying out careful measurements of the density of the photographic image along the entire length of the spectrum in order to discover in what part of the spectrum radiation is the most intense. A microscope-cum-photometer (microphotometer) is used for measuring and comparing the density of different sections of photographs, but even so the observations are not as straightforward as they might seem. In the first place allowance must be made for the altitude of the star above the horizon —the lower down it is the more the Earth's atmosphere will absorb some of the spectrum—and for the amount of haze or smoke present, since this affects the kind of absorption across the spectrum, some colours suffering more in this respect than others. Moreover Greaves had to determine how the photographic plate reacted to different colours in a far more precise way than any manufacturer needed to do, and even to determine what differences there were in the case of long exposures compared with shorter ones. It was a monumental task and took Greaves many years, but before he moved to Edinburgh he was able to publish detailed analyses for 250 stars and so provide the theoretical astronomer with some vital raw material for further research into the nature of stars and their generation of radiation. In Edinburgh with a new microphotometer designed and built in the observatory's workshops, Greaves continued and extended his work in the clearer atmosphere he found there.

The worsening of the atmosphere round Greenwich, noticeable towards the end of Christie's time, became more marked during the nineteen twenties and by the late thirties things had deteriorated to so marked a degree that the Astronomer Royal found grave cause for complaint. In many ways of course this was no wonder; when Charles II suggested Greenwich it was a small village in the heart of the country, but the growth of the railways as early as Airy's time began to make it possible for those who worked in London to move to homes outside it. The expansion of London was not uniform in the early days of the Industrial Revolution, and to begin with domestic building spread more readily to the west than to the south-east where Greenwich lay. The new light industries, too, began to mushroom mainly to the north-east of the city, and for a time Greenwich seemed to be escaping the worst effects of urban growth and retained something of its village character. But gradually, as the nineteenth century wore on, development occurred along the river banks, and power stations, situated where they could conveniently receive the sea-borne coal from the north-east of England, began to debase the skyline. In 1908 Christie could still claim that Melotte's discovery of the dim Jovian satellite showed[3] '.... the suitability of the Greenwich climate for the observation of very difficult objects such as faint satellites and close double stars.' He had averted the worst of the dangers caused by the power station on the meridian, but he could not hold back the tide. At the close of the First World War there were still green fields and country lanes within an easy walk of Greenwich, but by the late 1930's these were a thing of the past.

The problem was not that astronomers are countrymen who must avoid urbanised development, but the deleterious effects on observing that arise close to a city. Air pollution is one of the two more serious of these: it reduces the intensity of star-light reaching the telescopes, it leads to a great scattering of light within the telescope tube owing to the myriads of micro-scopic dust particles, and the constant bombardment of the apparatus by its chemically active constituents (such as sulphur dioxide) damages fine metal work like the pivots of transit instruments and the silvering on the mirrors of reflecting tele-scopes. It tarnishes the silver so quickly that, as Spencer Jones complained,[2] as soon as the 36-inch mirror had been re-silvered

'. . . its loss in reflecting power . . . can be measured from night to night'. Things had become so bad that an azimuth mark (a specially designed post), erected by Pond in 1824 at Chingford in Epping Forest to help him line up his transit instrument, was no longer visible because of the haze of air pollution. Even a 'clean air' policy could do little to ameliorate the Greenwich astronomer's woes, for the removal of soot particles is only part of the pollution problem, and, moreover, the Greenwich staff were also suffering from the effects of increasingly efficient street lighting. This brightened the night sky and reduced the contrast between stars and their background, again making it impossible to observe the dim stars that had been visible hitherto; and it produced a background light that made it impossible to take long exposure photographs—by the mid-thirties, in fact, it was not possible to look up at the sky and see even the Milky Way, let alone photograph it. In 1939 Spencer Jones reported to the Board of Visitors:[10] 'If the Royal Observatory is to continue to make important contributions to astronomy . . . it is essential that it should be removed to a site where astronomical conditions are favourable. The present wasteful efforts to secure observations under increasingly bad conditions and the restriction of the programmes that are necessitated by such conditions, would thereby be avoided.'

In the end Spencer Jones made his case, and various expedients were considered, but finally, with the wholehearted support of the Board of Visitors, the move of the entire establishment was agreed. Meanwhile Britain was embroiled in the Second World War, all astronomical observations that had no bearing on the war effort were suspended, and the majority of the staff found themselves occupied with other duties. It was a very different situation from that obtaining during the previous World War, when the observing programmes were continued even if sometimes under difficulties like Zeppelin raids. Now the great tradition of observing was broken and it was only after the war that Spencer Jones could gather his staff around him and take active steps to carry out the agreed move. The first task, of course, was to find a suitable site, somewhere that was away from electrified disturbances, far from the glare of city lights, with a clarity of atmosphere and prevailing meterological conditions that would favour the use of large telescopes.

South-east England was scoured for the appropriate place and only in 1946 was the choice finally made: the observatory, still with royal assent to be called the Royal Greenwich Observatory, was to move to Herstmonceux Castle, near Hailsham in Sussex.

It was a wise choice, for the site is on fairly high ground and there was plenty of space for the construction of an enlarged observatory, still leaving room for expansion in the 400-acre grounds. The castle itself, originally completed in 1440 for Sir Roger Feines, Lord High Treasurer to Henry VI, had been gutted in 1777 and rebuilt in 1913 and 1935. In 1948 Spencer Jones took up residence, followed by the solar and time departments and the staff of the *Nautical Almanac,* but the rest of the move was painfully slow. New buildings had to be designed, approved, and built, old apparatus taken down, cleaned, transported and set up again, and funds were scarce; thus it was not until the very end of 1958 that the move was completed and the new photographic zenith tube that Spencer Jones had longed to see was fitted in place. Now, almost twenty years after the war-time breakdown of the observatory, the observing programme could recommence; but Spencer Jones was unable to direct it, for he had reached retiring age in 1955, and had handed over to his sometime Chief Assistant Richard Woolley. But with the war over British astronomy had already entered a new phase, and with Woolley in charge, Greenwich again began to play a leading part.

X

The Way Ahead

IT IS ALWAYS dangerous to prophesy what will happen in the future. In science particularly the best of assessments are likely to be ruled out of court by some new and unforeseen discovery, some novel technique, or a combination of both which will deflect the mainstream of research into other channels. After 1945 there was a host of such techniques, developed in the war, which could be pressed into use for peaceful purposes; but it was only gradually realised that there were two with sufficient potential to transform astronomy in ways that could not have been contemplated or even imagined at the wildest meetings of scientific dining clubs. These were the use of the new-found radio techniques for handling very high radio frequencies, and the transformation of the German rocket bombs into launching vehicles for artificial satellites. They were to alter the whole face of astronomy and, by making it possible to probe the universe in new ways, to add immeasurably to our knowledge of what lies in space and how it is distributed.

To begin with, however, the end of the war seemed to bring astronomy no more than a return to freedom and a chance to assume research activities that had been suspended for far too long. The move of Greenwich Observatory was under way—in theory at least—and astronomers saw a golden opportunity, as they settled down to their work once more, for taking a fresh look at their profession and deciding what was required for post-war astronomy in Britain. The Royal Astronomical Society was the focal point of the new effort and in 1945 the president, Henry Plaskett,* holder of the Savilian chair of astronomy at Oxford, gave an address on the problem: it was an

---

* Dates of astronomers still living at the time of writing are not included.

address that startled many of his audience by its careful assessment of the facts and its refusal to be despondent over what appeared to be a rather gloomy situation. Plasket began by contrasting the university observatories in the United States with those in Britain and the comparison did no credit to university astronomy at Oxford, Cambridge or elsewhere. The University of Chicago possessed the world's largest refractor at its observatory at Williams Bay (Yerkes Observatory) and a substantial reflector in Texas also associated with it; the University of California had a giant refractor at Mount Hamilton (Lick Observatory), as well as a reflector that equalled anything in Britain; Harvard University had equipment at Cambridge far in exess of any British university observatory; while at the famous Mount Wilson Observatory associated with the California Institute of Technology there was the world's largest reflector, with an aperture of 100 inches, and, on nearby Mount Palomar, the giant 200-inch telescope was in the course of construction. It was catalogue as breathtaking in its length as mortifying in its implications. In Britain the two largest instruments, both 36-inch reflectors, were to be found at national observatories—at Edinburgh and Greenwich—and the future of university astronomy seemed most discouraging. The situation was indeed more unhappy when the size of university observatory staffs and ancillary equipment was taken into account, and the consequence, as Plaskett remarked, was that many of the British physicists and astronomers who had worked in the United States during the war were convinced that the situation was beyond remedy and thought that the only course was to concentrate on theoretical studies to the exclusion of everything else.

For a country to pursue theory without even the chance to undertake observation that could feed the theorist was a dangerous policy, more likely than not to spell disaster in the future. The theoretical work on the nature of the lines in stellar spectra that had been achieved in pre-war Britain by Edward Milne, Ralph Fowler (1889–1944), and the Indian physicist Meghnad Saha (1893–1956) had stemmed from the observations made by Huggins and Lockyer in particular, and, as Plaskett emphasised, Saha had come to Britain for the sole purpose of working on the problems of his choice close to the scene of their discovery. It was undoubtedly the case that the theorist wanted to be near the observatory to discuss matters with those who had actually seen the phenomena he was analysing. To limit British astronomers to theory alone would cause a 'brain drain' of terrifying proportions. Some action must be taken, some quite definite plans made, and the authorities alerted to the seriousness of the situation—this was the burden of Plaskett's exhortation. He himself straight away set about making definite proposals for a large telescope—about 74 inches, he suggested—which should be built in Britain as soon as possible and used conjointly by university astronomers. The cost—he had already obtained a rough estimate—should be in the region of £70,000—the kind of sum no one questioned when it was only a matter of the bricks and mortar for a new physics laboratory. Plaskett made his point: the Society decided to establish a committee, and elicit the help of the Royal Society in placing before the Government not only a plea for help but also a definite plan of action. It was here that there still remained points to be settled. If Britain was to have a large new telescope, precisely how large should it be, and what design details ought it to incorporate?

Two main lines of approach seemed possible. While everyone was agreed that the instrument should be a reflector— a refractor larger than 40 inches in aperture seemed impracticable, since this was the size of the Yerkes instrument which had been built in 1897 and the absorption of light through its thick lenses made it unlikely that apertures much greater would be able to add proportionally to the light-grasping power of the instrument—the question of the precise design of the reflector remained. It could be the ordinary well-tried design that had done duty ever since the days of Newton, with a parabolically curved mirror at one end and a secondary mirror at the other: such was the patterns on which the 110- and 200-inch reflectors in the United States had been designed and they presented only one drawback—a small sharply defined field of view. Such telescopes had great light-grasp, but because of their optical limitations they could only give a really sharp picture of a comparatively small area of the sky, the remainder being distorted. For detailed examination of one stellar spectrum this did not matter, for the main requirement here was a large light-grasp, so that there was sufficient light to allow wide dispersion and a consequently long and detailed spectrum; observations of the details of a nebula or a galaxy were also unaffected. But when it came to the determination of stellar parallax, the assessment of the number of stars in the sky and their individual motions, then large areas of the sky were better than small ones, since one photograph only need be taken instead of dozens, with consequent reduction in observing time and time spent in measurement. To overcome the small field limitation, it would be necessary to adopt the Schmidt design.

The Schmidt telescope had been evolved by Bernard Schmidt (1879–1935) in 1932 while working at the Hamburg Observatory, and consists of a spherically, not parabolically, curved main mirror and a smaller diameter lens at the front. The purpose of this front lens is to act as a corrector to the beams of light entering the mirror, so that they are all brought to the same focus without distortion; it acts on beams from a wide area of the sky and is therefore ideal for the kind of statistical studies that have just been mentioned. Its disadvantages are that its effective aperture is less than the conventional reflector and its light beams are brought to focus on a curved surface: for photography this presents no great problem, since a thin photographic plate can always be inserted into a curved plateholder, but in spectroscopy the smaller effective aperture and the curved focal surface can be troublesome. Plaskett, whose work and interests lay primarily in astrophysics, did not favour a Schmidt unless its design could be modified, possibly by removing the front lens and substituting a specially designed secondary mirror to return the reflector to the more conventional type at will.

The argument that there was nowhere in Britain with a clear enough atmosphere to make the use of a large aperture instrument either effective or worthwhile was a myth and was soon demolished, but the design of the telescope was a very different matter. The editors of the *Observatory* magazine, all of them professional astronomers, plumped wholeheartedly for the straightforward reflector and eschewed the idea of a large Schmidt, arguing that it was in spectroscopy that the really big telescope was most needed in Britain. There was, they pointed out, a large Schmidt telescope being constructed in

211

the United States, and a small Schmidt would surely do for Britain? They did however make one vital point that was not to be neglected: the money voted—if voted at all—must be sufficient to provide not only the telescope but also such ancillary equipment as spectroscopic work demands and an adequate staff. Better a slightly smaller telescope fully equipped and properly manned than a giant instrument that is but little used because it is insufficiently endowed.

In the event money for the project was agreed before the design had been decided although by the time the project had passed through the Royal Society and found its way to the Chancellor, Spencer Jones had convinced both his colleagues and the Treasury that an instrument of 100 inches aperture was to be recommended rather than the more modest 75 inches that Plaskett had suggested. It was also decided that the project should be named the Isaac Newton Observatory or the Newton Memorial Observatory, to mark the celebration of the tercentenary of Newton's birth. With the added support of the Astronomer Royal for Scotland the project moved far and fast, but broadened by the proviso that the new instrument should be available to all suitably qualified British astronomers and not limited to those whose work was carried out in university departments. Hopes ran high, Parliament agreed to the Chancellor's proposals and by the end of 1946, five months after Plaskett's original suggestions, discussion about the detailed design were under way. With the completion of a 74-inch telescope at the Radcliffe Observatory in South Africa, the prospects for British astronomy in both northern and southern hemispheres appeared bright once more.

Delays in the completion of the new telescope have been long—rather longer than expected. Much time was spent on the design considerations, the double design that Plaskett suggested being studied in detail, but finally, in 1956, agreement was reached on a conventional telescope with wide facilities to enable it to be used for as many lines of research as possible. Although no one begrudged the effort spent on the design, it was not long completed before the financial situation made it necessary to suspend further work for a year. However in 1949, long before the design was finished, British astronomy had a stroke of luck: the trustees of the McGregor Fund of the University of

212

Michigan had presented a 98-inch glass disk to Spencer Jones for a project, a disk that had been intended for a large reflector at Michigan and never used, and it is this that has been incorporated into the Isaac Newton telescope. Spencer Jones has been criticised for some of the delays, but it seems unlikely that a man with his considerable experience as an administrator of large observatories in South Africa and at Greenwich would not have done everything possible to push things forward. Financial difficulties and other problems resulted in intermittent efforts of the kind only too evident in many enterprises in this country since the war. Certainly while the move of Greenwich to its new home in Sussex was taking place, Spencer Jones spent much time and no little effort in work for the International Astronomical Union—a body for co-operative planning of astronomy founded in 1922—and in what can best be described as astronomical diplomacy abroad. As astronomy is, and always has been, a supra-national activity his efforts in this direction can have been nothing less than helpful.

If the new optical telescope for British astronomy has taken its time to appear, there are other research projects which have by their nature gone ahead more quickly and have kept British astronomers on their toes. The first of these to appear has been a direct result of wartime research and, in Britain at least, has evolved from the development and use of radar. This technique of radiating very short pulses of ultra-high-frequency radio waves and receiving back their echoes, a vital means of ranging on enemy aircraft, has, naturally enough, since been developed to aid shipping and help aircraft; but at the end of hostilities, before the commercial expansion of radar could commence, there were a large number of radar stations scattered over the country, staffed to capacity but with little to do. It was through the genius of Edward Appleton (1892–1965) and James Hey that the equipment was used for tracking meteors instead of lying idle, and a thorough survey of their appearance was instituted. The results obtained were of considerable benefit to astronomers since radar tracking made it possible to observe meteors in daylight as well as at night, observations that were impossible with any visual equipment since a meteor trail is usually dim and invisible against the glare of the daylight sky. The results

213

showed the frequency of daylight meteors, went some way towards broadening the picture of meteor orbits, and began to show the value of this kind of technique. They were followed up by a research team of the University of Manchester, which had established an experimental station at Jodrell Bank near Macclesfield; this further research helped to clear up the problem of whether meteors were part of the solar system or whether they were from further afield. Optical observations had provided no unequivocal answer but had certainly made it seem probable that some, and perhaps the majority, came from interstellar space: yet it was still necessary to determine a great number of meteor velocities, since interstellar meteors must possess high velocities, while for those within the solar system velocities would be much smaller, and proper statistical evidence was required to come to a conclusion. It was Bernard Lovell and his colleagues at Jodrell Bank who were able to clear up the problem as the radar technique was an ideal method for readily determining meteor velocity, and in 1950 they found that the majority were certainly slow enough to make it certain that that they were from the solar system: not more than one per cent could be from instellar space.

In spite of its apparent promise, radar was limited in its application to astronomy, since a radio pulse disperses to some extent on its journey into space as well as on its return, thus losing energy, while at reflection some of the power is absorbed. Moreover in the case of astronomical distances, these are so great that the time taken by a pulse to go out and return again will be measured in years for any object outside the solar system, since radio waves have the same velocity as light. In consequence it is unreasonable to suppose that radar can be used for probing deep into space—even to the nearest star an observer would be forced to wait for nine years before receiving his radio pulse back, and over such a distance its energy might all have been dissipated. Within the solar system the situation is rather different, and radar pulses were bounced off the Moon in 1946 by American scientists working with the United States Signal Corps, permitting its distance to be found with high accuracy; this work was extended at Jodrell Bank to investigate details of the lunar orbit. Later both at Jodrell Bank and in the United States, the technique was applied to Venus when it

214

made a close approach to the Earth, and the results were used for determining the distance Earth to Sun with a degree of accuracy superior even to that obtained from Eros by Spencer Jones and Melotte: it gave a figure for the Sun's distance of a little less than they had obtained and did so with an error of no more than 160 miles.

Although radar is limited in its astronomical range, there is another aspect of ultra-high-frequency radio studies that is not, and this is the examination of the radio waves that are emitted by celestial bodies themselves. As far back as 1931 Karl Jansky, working for the Bell Telephone Laboratories in New Jersey on the problem of crackling or 'static' noise which marred short-wave radio transmission, discovered that there was some correlation between this noise and the position of the Sun in the sky as well as from somewhere in the area of the constellation Sagittarius, although his later work did not seem to show any correlation with the position of the Sun as he had first believed. Little more might have been done had not a special 'directional' radio aerial, more precise in its ability to determine the true direction of a source of radio waves, been set up in New Jersey in 1935 for the express purpose of receiving radio signals from England. Again 'cosmic static' as it was then called was picked up now and again but little notice was paid to the phenomenon until Grote Reber, an American amateur astronomer, decided to investigate the subject. He learned privately that work at the California Institute of Technology had confirmed Jansky's results and decided to build himself a special radio aerial that was highly directional in the signals it would receive, fixed in azimuth but free to move in altitude, and made in the form of a metal dish 31 feet in diameter. With this 'radio telescope' Reber began his observing programme, and confirmed first that there appeared to be a strong source of radio radiation in that part of Sagittarius where the Milky Way lies and also at various other points along the Milky Way itself. But little was done to follow up Reber's results, probably because, like Jansky's, they were published in technical scientific journals read by radio engineers and seldom if ever glanced at by astronomers.

The post-war situation was different because Hey and his colleagues at the Royal Radar Esablishment at Malvern were trained radio engineers, and with the end of the war and stores to hand, they decided to modify the equipment and use it to investigate cosmic noise: the results were surprising and of the utmost significance. To begin with they found, as Jansky and others had done, that radio radiation was received from the Sagittarius area and from the constellation of Cygnus; they measured the strength of the radiation and found that it was low but nevertheless quite definite, with no possibility of its arising from any terrestrial source. The stars—or something connected with them—were radiating radio waves as well as radiating light, heat and ultra-violet radiation, and they began to pursue their investigations further. They tracked down the source of radiation in Cygnus to an area of sky about two degrees across and, as with their other results, published news of the discovery in *Nature,* where it was likely to reach a wider and more catholic-minded readership than in a technical electronic periodical.

In the same year, 1946, Appleton and Hey began to ex-amine the radio radiation from the Sun, a body with a known temperature of some 6,000 degrees Centigrade for its surface gases which, in theory at least, might be expected to emit radio waves as well as the usual radiation. They found, as Appleton later put it,[1] 'that big sunspots were extemely power-ful ultra-short wave [i.e. ultra-high-frequency] radio transmitters, the radiation received on earth being very greatly in excess of the expected black-body radiation'; in other words, the emission of radio frequencies from sunspots was far greater than to be expected from a gaseous body like the Sun which to the physicist was a 'black body', that is one in which the quality and quantity of radiation depends only on temperature and and which, if cold, would appear perfectly black. Moreover they found that bursts of this solar radio 'noise' were associated with the appearance on the solar disk of bright flares of hot gas and with effects that disturbed the electrified layers of air high above the Earth, causing a fade-out in short-wave wireless communication used especially by shipping and already well known to radio operators. Then a second discovery was made: on certain wavelengths the Sun, even without the pres-ence of large spots and bright flares—the quiescent Sun as astronomers call it—emitted radio waves more strongly than theory suggested it should. 'In this connection', said Appleton,[2] 'we therefore have to speak of "quiet solar noise"!' Radio engineers and astronomers were by now alerted to a new series of phenomena that did not appear to be catered for by theory. Research was stimulated, other investigators as far afield as Australia, New Zealand, the United States, Canada, and Britain began to take up the problem, and 'radio astronomy' was born.

This new sphere of research began to gather momentum so speedily and with such vigour that it will be impossible to follow it in detail further here, even confining ourselves to the British contributions alone: the best we can do is to underline one or two of the main trends in this work in the last two decades. It is encouraging, though, to realise that the three leaders in this completely new field of research have been the Australian team centred at the Commonwealth Scientific and Industrial Research Organisation station at Parkes near Sydney, the Cavendish Laboratory team at Lords Bridge, Cambridge and the Manchester University centre at Jodrell Bank. Perhaps the fact that both Australia and Britain at this time lagged well behind the United States in power as far as conventional optical telescopes were concerned may have had more than a little to do with the sudden upsurge in radio astronomy, but whatever the cause, the results have been both spectacular and, astronomically speaking, of the most profound significance.

The basic problem that faced the radio astronomer was the need to achieve a substantial improvement in resolution. It was all very well to be able to discover, as Hey had done, that there was a radio source in Cygnus within an area of sky about two degrees across, but this was little help to the conventional astronomer or even to the radio astronomer who wished to find what kind of object it was that emitted such strong ultra-high-frequency radiation. There must after all be some link between what was well established and what was new if the science of astronomy was not to be split in two by a novel observing technique—but the solution of the problem was not easy. Radio waves used in radio astronomy cover a wide range, but, roughly speaking, are at least fifty thousand times larger than the light waves received by an optical telescope. In consequence, a radio telescope needs a curved reflector or dish fifty thousand times larger than its optical counterpart if it is to possess the same degree of resolution and permit the radio astronomer to pinpoint radio sources with the same precision as the conventional astronomer. For a radio telescope to be equivalent in size to the 36-inch reflectors at Edinburgh and Greenwich this would mean an aperture of 200 miles, and this for some of the shortest radio waves studied by radio astronomers: the longer waves used in some observations would require an even larger instrument! The situation is not as hopeless as it sounds, however, for provided that resolution can come down to a few hundred times that of an optical telescope, the optical astronomer can obtain enough detailed knowledge to identify the sources of radio waves from his photographs, and the most awkward obstacle is removed.

One obvious way to tackle the problem of resolution is to build a radio telescope with a really big reflector, since such an instrument can give a resolution measured in minutes of arc rather than in degrees, and this method was one of those that Lovell decided to develop at Jodrell Bank. His conception was on a grand scale, and with the assistance of a local firm of consultant engineers rough plans were drawn up for the construction of a radio telescope with a reflecting bowl with the unprecedented diameter of 250 feet: it was to be mounted between two towers, each a little higher than Nelson's column, with the whole instrument supported by a framework running on a specially designed circular railway track. Technically this would provide an altazimuth mounting which demanded two separate movements to follow radio sources as they travelled, like the stars, across the sky—a bane to the optical astronomer but nowhere near such a disadvantage to the radio astronomer, whose equipment is essentially electronically controlled so that the amounts of both movements can be worked out automatically on a computer and applied to the telescope direct. Even though the curvature of the bowl of the reflector did not have to be finished with the high degree of accuracy that is necessary for a mirror, because of the long wavelength of radio waves compared with light waves, the engineering difficulties were still enormous. The bowl's purpose was similar to that of a telescope mirror— to collect incoming radio waves and bring them to a focus— and it needed to be strongly enough braced to keep its shape within a fraction of an inch in whatever direction it might be pointing, and to be firm enough to withstand strong winds since it was too large to mount inside an observatory dome. To begin with, the surface of the bowl was to be covered with close mesh wire netting, a quite inadequate reflector for light but satisfactory enough for the radio waves, which would be too long to slip through the openings; but before building was complete it became clear that shorter wavelengths must also be received and the bowl was covered inside with sheets of metal. The radio telescope, however, has one constructional advantage over an optical telescope: it does not require a long tube above the reflector and the dish has merely to bring the radio waves to focus on a special aerial, to all outward appearances little different from the ubiquitous television aerial.

Lovell's conception, which was staggering in its boldness, called for funds far beyond any that the university could spare and he was forced to use every power of persuasion to try to solicit outside support. In 1955 he visited the Department of Scientific and Industrial Research and the Nuffield Foundation and in the event extracted a total of almost a quarter of a million pounds from each—more than five times the amount earmarked for the Isaac Newton telescope—and the project was under way. Early in 1957 he could report that the main structural steel work of the instrument had been completed and the driving mechanism was nearly ready so that the telescope should be 'in its fully steerable operational condition by midsummer...';[2] and the next year, it was quietly and calmly announced that this triumph of British engineering and electronics skill 'met all expectations', performing with results of an accuracy close to what had been predicted theoretically. The giant size of the Jodrell Bank radio telescope captured popular imagination and helped materially in the revival of a general interest in astronomy, an interest very necessary if public funds are to be diverted from less worthy purposes and applied to the discovery of the universe. This popular support was increased by the dramatic use of the instrument to track the Russian and American space probes launched since 1959 towards the Moon: satellites made news and the 250-foot telescope became a symbol of Britain's participation in the exploration of space.

The huge radio telescope that could be steered to point in any direction was not only the solution to the radio astronomers' problem of resolution: there was another quite different approach which made use of two or more small radio telescopes working in conjunction. The essence of the method is to observe a particular source of radio waves in the sky with at least two radio telescopes and then mix the radio signals that they receive so that these interfere with one another; as radio telescopes are directional and only receive strong signals from the direction in which they point, their resolution is increased by mixing and, what is more, increased to a degree not proportional to the size of the telescopes but to the distance between them. A pair of telescopes each, say, 40 feet in diameter and separated by a quarter of a mile, will be equivalent when used as an 'interfero-meter' not to a 80-foot telescope but to one a quarter of a mile across. For complete pinpointing of a celestial source it turns out that at least four telescopes are needed, two to increase resolution in one direction and two to increase it in the other, thus allowing the position of the source to be determined in a way that will leave little doubt in the mind of the optical astro-nomer who wants to photograph the source. Optical confirma-tion is, of course, necessary because a radio telescope produces no image that one can see, no picture that past experience can recognise as a star, a galaxy, or a nebula; all that arrives is a measure of the strength of radio radiation and although this may be plotted on a chart, the plot does no more than give the position—it says nothing about the nature of the source.

The interferometer radio telescope was developed with much vigour in Australia and in Britain, and its use has since become standard practice at radio astronomical observatories. In Britain it was at Cambridge that Martin Ryle and his team early began to explore the possibilities of interferometer arrangements, and by 1951 a total of some one hundred radio sources were charted and the interferometer technique was beginning to make itself known. Graham Smith, one of Ryle's associates, had succeeded in measuring the position of two of the strongest radio sources—in Cygnus and in Cassiopeia—with an accuracy of forty-five seconds of arc in one direction and ten seconds in the other: a reduction of about one hundred times the previous uncertainty and perfectly adequate to permit an astronomer to direct a tele-scope as large as the 200-inch to a specific point in the sky. In fact this is what happened next, for in 1952 Walter Baade

(1893–1960) at Mount Palomar took photographs at selected points and examined the objects that were causing the radio radiation. They proved to be unusual. The source in Cassiopeia was found to be a strange nebula lying within our own galaxy; it was spherical and formed of five filaments, all of which showed high-speed motions when their light was analysed in the spectroscope. But if the source in Cassiopeia was unusual, that in Cygnus proved to be an even greater surprise: the radio radiation was found to be coming from a remote spiral galaxy, situated some two hundred million light-years beyond our own. Nor was it a straightforward galaxy, for Baade's photographs and spectroscopic studies showed peculiarities never observed before: about half its light was coming from a vast cloud of interstellar gas within it, and it seemed just as if it might be not one galaxy but two in collision. In Australia on the other hand, it had been suggested that there was a correlation between the next two most intense radio sources and known optical objects; one was in the Crab nebula—the remains of a supernova explosion that had originally occurred in 1054 A.D.—and the other was a peculiar elliptical galaxy, quite different from the spiral object identified with the Cambridge observations.

The first four radio sources identified each proved to be a different kind of object—a nebula, a distant spiral galaxy, supernova remnants, and a remote elliptical galaxy—and in every case there was something unusual about the source. Clearly here was a situation that required further examination, and it was obvious that all the other radio sources needed identifying as soon as possible. It was unlikely that they would all prove to be peculiar in one way or another but it was imperative that they should be examined optically as well as with radio telescopes. Ryle therefore decided to build a new and improved interfero-meter, using four large radio telescopes each built in the form of a long narrow trough, the curve of the trough being shaped to bring the radio waves to focus on a number of television-type aerials spread along it. Each trough-shaped aerial was 350 feet long and the four were spread out in two pairs, over an area of a little more than one acre. These radio telescopes could be tilted from side to side and thus be pointed to any altitude: they would then require no other motion since the Earth's rotation would allow them to sweep the sky. Early in

1953 this new interferometer was ready and John Shakeshaft and John Baldwin made a survey of almost two thousand radio sources, obtaining positions of five hundred with sufficient accuracy to allow optical identification. David Dewhirst at the Cambridge University Observatories, which had recently acquired a Schmidt telescope with a 24-inch mirror, began to check the brighter objects, and some of the others were examined at Mount Palomar. Again a number of peculiar objects such as colliding—or possibly splitting—spiral galaxies were discovered, but by and large it was clear by 1955 that even bigger equipment more suitable for resolving faint sources was needed, and Ryle and his colleagues turned to a more elaborate form of interferometer, which worked by what is known as 'aperture synthesis'. Basically this is a method of using one or two fixed radio telescopes and another that can move with respect to them: observations of the radio sources being investigated are made with the movable telescope in one position, another series of observations are then completed with the movable instrument in another position, and gradually the whole area between fixed and movable telescopes is filled in. The results are then analysed by computer. This technique has proved so useful that Ryle has built an aperture synthesis equipment, the most advanced in the world at the time of writing, which comprises three 60-foot diameter radio telescopes electrically linked and giving an effective aperture of one mile in diameter, and with this the fainter radio sources are being studied.

Meanwhile other investigations have been made at Jodrell Bank, and these have included studies of the kind of interstellar gas which is invisible in optical telescopes but readily observable by radio, studies which have led to a fuller understanding of the distribution of gas within our own galaxy and of its shape and rotation. Deep probing into space has also been carried out using the 250-foot radio telescope coupled to a smaller instrument situated at a distance of more than a hundred miles. Here the investigations have been aimed at trying to determine precisely how large an area of the sky is covered by each of the separate sources whose position has been charted with the aperture synthesis equipment at Cambridge, and they are of vital importance for the new studies recently made by

222

cosmologists who have been attempting to formulate theories of the universe as a whole.

In the years following the Second World War a quartet of mathematical astronomers at Cambridge, Herman Bondi, Thomas Gold, Fred Hoyle and Raymond Lyttleton, began to look into the theory of relativity and the mathematical equations that Einstein had derived from it. As intimated in the previous chapter, the theory of relativity gives rise to a host of mathematical equations that express the behaviour of the universe and it is not yet possible to be sure, in any set of equations, whether they do in fact represent the universe as we observe it to be. Some show the universe to be expanding; others lead to the conclusion that the universe oscillates, a period of expansion following a period of contraction, after which the cycle is repeated again and again; while there is a third class of theory which can be derived if the equations are handled in a particular way, as Bondi, Gold, Hoyle and Lyttleton managed to do. Their theory is known as the 'steady-state' cosmology and provides a type of static universe in which change is only a local and limited process.

The steady-state hypothesis was derived from relativity because, on working through the mathematical consequences, the four mathematicians found that they arrived at an apparently anomalous result, namely that in any given volume of space, in any section of the entire universe they liked to take, the quantity of material always remained the same. Such a result would not have given Wright, Herschel or even Lockyer any grave qualms, but to the twentieth-century astronomer it seemed completely at odds with observations: every photograph of the spectrum of a distant galaxy showed an undeniable red shift of the spectral lines, indicating that the objects are moving away from us as observers, receding at immense velocities away from our galaxy. But did this theoretical result perhaps mean that the supposition that the red shifts were due to motion away in the line of sight was not valid for the vast distances involved with the far-off galaxies, and if it did not, what was the cause of this undeniable movement of all spectral lines away from the blue and towards the red?

Various attempts were made to try to find alternatives. The

red shift predicted by Einstein's relativity theory as the result of the gravitational pulls of large bodies like stars, was nowhere near large enough to account for the magnitude of shift actually observed; nor was the shift computed by Edward Milne on the basis of his theory of kinematical relativity. Here a red shift was to be expected, since atomic processes operated according to a basic time-scale while our observations were made on a local time-scale, and the result of the two would give rise to an apparent loss of energy and so an apparent shift of the spectral lines to the red (lower energy). But again, the Milne shift was too small to account for the observations. The possibility of the loss of energy by the light itself on so long a journey through space was also investigated by Erwin Finlay Freundlich (1885–1964), the first professor of astronomy at St Andrews University, but his suggestions about the nature of this loss appeared to bring in other factors that were at variance with observation; while suggestions that the shift was only apparent and due to the nature of space itself—made by Eric Holmberg again did not find general acceptance among astronomers. There seemed nothing for it but to accept the spectral line shift—or most of it at any rate—as a consequence of recession, as a result in fact of the very causes that Doppler and Fizeau had worked out nearly a century ago.

The Cambridge mathematicians accepted this interpretation of the reality of recession and had therefore to postulate a replacement process if their theory was not to be rejected: if recession took place no section of space could contain the same amount of material unless it was somehow constantly fed with a fresh supply. For this they proposed in 1949 the concept of 'continuous creation', suggesting that the basic particles of atoms are continually forming in the universe and forming at a rate just sufficient to replace the material that is moving away owing to expansion. No explanation was given or could at that time be offered about the kind of physical process involved in the creation of matter from nothing, and, moreover, their calculations showed that if the process were occurring as they suggested, it would be on too small a scale to be observable. Here then was a theory that appeared to be dependent only on mathematics and to be divorced from physical reality in that it postulated a physical process—the continuous creation of matter—that seemed to do violence to all normal laws of nature as generally accepted by the scientific world. In addition it did away with any belief in the beginning or end of the universe: matter was always being created, had always been and would always be, the universe presented the same picture at all times—past, present and future—and was in consequence eternal both back and forth in time. This is what a steady-state ultimately meant.

So novel and unusual a theory came in for immediate and heavy attack—one critic going so far as to say that it betrayed a profound ignorance of the nature of science—but gradually the storms subsided and it became clear that the issue was really to try to find some observational confirmation or denial for the steady-state situation. The alternative theory, proposed by the Abbé Lemaître between 1933 and 1934 in Belgium and in a modified but similar form by George Gamov in 1948 in the United States, postulated an original state of the universe, soon after 'creation', in which all the material was closely packed together: thereafter expansion was believed to have occurred through the break-up of so highly concentrated a state of affairs, on the analogy of the break-up of heavy atoms as evinced in radioactive substances like radium and uranium. The process of original creation was not discussed in these theories any more than it was in the steady-state cosmology (where in any case it never occurred and was irrelevant): this however did not worry any astronomer, for as Eddington had once pointed out, so singular an act of creation was not amenable to scientific scrutiny.

For observational proof or disproof the astronomer had to look far afield, since the steady-state cosmologists claimed that their hypothesis was valid only if a very large volume of the universe were considered, a volume that contained a prodigious number of galaxies: it was a statistical theory and required a large sample to make sense. Moreover, if the observational astronomer looked far into the depths of space there was another factor that might help him in his choice between the two types of cosmology—the factor of time. This arises because the more distant an object is in space, the longer its light (or its radio waves) have taken to reach us, and therefore the further into space we probe the further back in time we go. On the Gamov-

225

Lemaître type of cosmology—the so-called 'big bang' theories of a cosmic explosion—the moment of creation is calculated to have been, approximately, some ten thousand million years ago; consequently if their theory is correct then observations of distant galaxies four or five thousand million light-years away in space will show the universe as it was half-way back to creation —in other words they will show a universe that had not expanded as much as it has done now. The obvious conclusion, then, is that in such far distant realms of space we see the universe as it was when the galaxies were closer together than they are at present, and distant parts of space should therefore appear more crowded than those closer to us in time. On the steady-state cosmology, however, we should notice no such crowding, since for all time and at all times the universe is assumed to look the same: old galaxies pass out of sight and new ones form from the matter continuously being created. Here then would appear to be an escape from our dilemma—we have only to observe and see whether or no there is evidence of galaxies crowding one another in distant space.

It is to the radio astronomer that the evidence has seemed to point to a crowding of galaxies. With the technique of the large interferometer and the aperture synthesis equipment, there seems at the present time to be some support for the belief that the universe gives evidence of evolution from a primary explosion rather than from a statistically steady state. Admittedly the evidence is not yet conclusive and some modifications of the steady-state cosmology have so far managed to make a small amount of crowding acceptable; but the general climate of opinion seems to be that this cosmology is up against grave observational difficulties, if not yet facing observational disproof. Nevertheless the position is not yet clear and for two reasons. In the first place William McCrea has recently put forward the concept of *continual* (not continuous) creation, suggesting that new matter is formed within galaxies and not evenly throughout space—a proposal that would modify the idea of a steady-state picture even more, and one that appears to have some observational evidence to support it. Optical examination with the 200-inch at Mount Palomar has shown that many of the strong sources of radio emission are distant galaxies that are undergoing the most violent eruptions within and seem to be ejecting material which may (or may not) turn out to be embryonic galaxies. Secondly, a whole new class of celestial object—the 'quasar'—has been discovered.

Quasars (an abbreviated name for Quasi-Stellar-Radio-Sources) are objects that emit strongly at radio wavelengths but give every appearance in an optical telescope of being stars. The mystery about them lies in the fact that every quasar so far examined shows the most immense red shift of its spectral lines, and since on the accepted view of an expanding universe, large red shift means that we are observing over a very great distance (since the velocity of objects increases the greater the distance they are away), these objects cannot be ordinary stars. Though they look like them they emit radio waves to a degree that is wildly excessive and quite impossible for a star: they are, however, smaller in size than any normal galaxy. Various suggestions have been made to account for them: Margaret and Geoffrey Burbidge, two British astronomers who worked in the United States for some years, have suggested the possibility that the objects were small galaxies troubled with a sudden excess of supernova explosions; Fred Hoyle has investigated the possibility that quasars are distant bodies that have collapsed under their own vast gravitational pull; and in the United States Jesse Greenstein and Maarten Schmidt have proposed that a quasar is an extraordinarily hot and very dense cloud of gas. Yet whatever the outcome of these proposals, it seems very likely that the discovery of quasars and the further research of radio astronomers will lead to a re-assessment of the cosmological picture. The steady-state cosmology may go, but the research it has stimulated will, as with previous theories of cosmology, be of lasting value.

Another form of speculative theory in which British astronomers have taken an active part has been the question of formation of the solar system. Kant and Laplace made a bold attempt to attack the problem in the latter part of the eighteenth century, but it was in the closing decades of the nineteenth century that the subject was opened up again after the intellectual bombshell of evolutionary theory had burst upon the scientific world. Appropriately enough it was George Darwin, son of the famous biologist, who from 1879 onwards made a series of studies of the mathematics of the tides and thus of the gravita-

227

tional attraction between the Earth and the Moon, and came
to the conclusion that the Earth and Moon had once formed a
single body, the Moon later breaking away owing to the forces
generated by the Earth's rotation, more rapid in the past than
now. This work caused some interest in the United States and
on the Continent but it was not extended to the wider question
of the formation of the planets until the early years of the
twentieth century, when Thomas Chamberlin (1843–1928) and
Foust Ray Moulton (1872–1912) in Chicago suggested that
it now seemed more than likely that Laplace had been wrong.
They suggested that the solar system was formed from material
drawn out of the Sun by tidal forces caused by the close approach
of another star which, after the disruptions, continued on its
way through space and was now unrecognisable. Jeans and
Eddington gave them every support and pointed out the corollary of this theory—the rarity of the solar system: as Jeans
put it,[3] '... calculation shows that even after a star has lived
its life of millions of millions of years, the chance is still
about a hundred thousand to one against its being surrounded
by planets'.

More recently alternative theories have swept away the 'close
approach' hypothesis, so that general opinion has turned from
belief in a catastrophic occurrence to the likelihood that the
formation of the planets round a star is the rule rather than
the exception. Kenneth Edgeworth and Fred Hoyle have put
forward theories which consider the planets to have been formed
at the same time as the Sun itself and Hoyle (working with
the American nuclear physicist William Fowler) has gone further, to investigate how if the Sun, like other stars, was mainly
formed of hydrogen, all the heavier chemical elements found in
the solar system could have been synthesised. More recently
still, in 1964, they have extended their work to the synthesis
of the heavier elements inside the massive stars and supernovae. The detailed calculations involved can now be managed
by computer and it is encouraging to find that the Nuffield
Foundation and the Scientific Research Council have each set
aside a quarter of a million pounds to establish an Institute of
Theoretical Astronomy in Cambridge so that Hoyle and others
can continue work of this kind and also investigate the new
theories of gravitation which are rising to the surface.

Theory must always be founded on observation and corrected by newly acquired observational results: otherwise we shall return to the outlook prevalent before the beginnings of astronomy in Britain, when theory ruled alone and any scheme, wild or sane, could gain a following. In the twentieth century the growth of observing techniques has extended phenomenally —the radio astronomer has opened up a vast new window into space, a window through which results are flooding in, since cloudy and hazy weather do not impede radio waves as they do light, while automatic recording of results made both in daylight and at night means that extensive surveys of the sky may be continuously made. Yet radio astronomy is only one new sector of astronomical observation; the use of rocket-launched space probes is also extending knowledge to parts of the spectrum that never reach the Earth-based observatories. X-rays and very short-wave ultra-violet radiation are emitted from the gas, stars, and galaxies in various parts of space, yet this radiation has always been unobservable because of the blanketing effect of the Earth's atmosphere which absorbs this entire range. Only now, with the development of rocketry, can telescopes and spectroscopes be launched into space to observe the universe at the new short wavelengths as well as in certain long radio wavelengths and parts of the infra-red that are also blacked out by atmospheric absorption. Unfortunately the expense involved in programmes of this kind has ruled Britain out of the race as a major competitor, but a few useful results have been achieved using a small rocket launched from the Australian rocket range at Woomera and advantage has been taken of American offers to launch satellites containing British instruments. In this way X-ray telescopes designed by Robert Boyd and his colleagues at London University, and equipment prepared at other British universities including a long-wave radio telescope designed by Graham Smith, have been put into orbit round the Earth. The results have been most valuable. Co-operation with the French astronomer Audouin Dollfus by David Dewhirst and Donald Blackwell has also extended observational evidence on the nature of the Sun's surface gases by taking photographs from a manned balloon that has risen above the thicker parts of the atmosphere; but as with rocket developments, it is the Americans who have led in this field by launching balloons with remote controlled television and photographic equipment.

Yet exciting and important though these new developments in extra-terrestrial observing are, it is the solid observational and theoretical work back on Earth that is the mainstay of astronomy. Observations of a new kind must always be correlated with the solid facts we know and which have been acquired slowly and laboriously over the years. Variable stars, studied with increasing application ever since the work of Goodricke two centuries ago, are still fruitful fields of research, as the present Astronomer Royal is only too well aware, and under him a special research programme is going ahead. And even in these days of government and foundation support for research and the use of expensive and elaborate equipment by the professional, the amateur is managing to continue the tradition, so strong in Britain, of making worthwhile additions to the observational evidence on which the professional can base his theories: in lunar studies, observations of the Sun, of meteors, comets and planets, and even in the fields of variable star work and radio astronomy, they are still busy and productive. There is, in fact, no doubt that at every level British astronomers will continue to play their part, as they have always done, but integrated now into the great international research effort that is modern astronomy: integrated, but not submerged, any more than their predecessors have been.

References

CHAPTER II

1   From R. Norton's English translation quoted in F. R.
    Johnson, *Astronomical Thought in Renaissance England*,
    Baltimore and London, 1932.
2   Thomas Digges, *A Perfit Description. . . .*, signatures Ml^r to
    Ml^v, London, 1576.
3   Robert Recorde, *Castle of Knowledge*, London, 1556,
    p. 127. (This, as F. R. Johnson points out, is misnumbered
    in the printed edition as p. 129.)
4   From a translation by F. R. Johnson, *op. cit.*, p. 159.
5   From a translation by Frances Yates in her *Giordano Bruno
    and the Hermetic Tradition*, London, 1964, p. 236.
6   *Ibid.*, p. 242.
7   John Dee, preface to H. Billingsley, *The Elements of
    Geometrie of the most auncient Philosopher Euclide of
    Megara*, London, 1570.
8   *Ibid.*
9   William Gilbert, *De Magnete*, translated by P. Fleury
    Mottelay, New York, 1958, p. 69.
10 John Wallis, *A Defence of the Royal Society, and the
    Philosophical Transactions particularly those of July* 1670
    in answer to the cavils of Dr William Holder, London,
    1678.
11 *Journal Book of the Royal Society*, **I**. 1600.
12 *Ibid.*

CHAPTER III

1   Newton in a letter to John Collins, *The Correspondence of
    Isaac Newton*, **I**, Cambridge, 1959 p. 161.
2   James Gregory in a letter to John Collins, *ibid.*, **I**, p. 259.

3 Memorandum in the *Portsmouth Collection,* section I, division X, number 41, (A collection of Newton's papers originally in the possession of the Earl of Portsmouth but sold in 1936).

4 Horace, *Epistles,* **I**, i, lines 13–14.

CHAPTER IV

1 From a manuscript draft by Newton of a letter, now in the University of Cambridge Library, Add. 3968.41.85^r

2 *The Correspondence of Isaac Newton,* **II**, p. 297.

3 *Ibid.,* **II**, p. 431.

4 *Ibid.,* **II**, p. 433.

5 *Ibid.,* **II**, p. 437.

6 *Ibid.,* **III**, p. 240.

7 Edmond Halley, *Astronomical Tables,* London, 1752.

8 *Philosophical Transactions,* **29**, p. 390.

9 *Ibid.,* **30**, p. 736.

10 *Ibid.,* **31**, p. 22.

CHAPTER V

1 William Herschel, *Collected Scientific Papers,* **I**, London, 1912, p. xix.

2 *Ibid.,* **I**, p. xxii.

3 *Ibid.,* **I**, p. xxix.

4 *Ibid.,* **I**, p. xxx.

5 *Ibid.,* **I**, p. xxxv.

6 *Ibid.,* **I**, p. xlvii.

7 *Ibid.,* **I**, p. 337.

8 *Ibid.,* **II**, p. 541.

9 *Ibid.,* **II**, p. 527.

10 *Scientific Papers of William Parsons, Third Earl of Rosse,* London, 1926, p. 21.

11 W. Airy (ed), *Autobiography of Sir George Airy,* Cambridge, 1896, p. 198.

12 *Scientific Papers of William Parsons, etc.,* p. 29.

13 S. Smiles (ed.), *James Nasmyth, an Autobiography,* London, 1883, p. 326.

CHAPTER VI

1 *Occasional Notes of the Royal Astronomical Society,* **2**, 1947, p. 43.
2 *Ibid.,* p. 47.
3 *Monthly Notices of the Royal Astronomical Society,* **7**, 1847 p. 121.
4 *Occasional Notes etc.,* **2**, 1947, p. 67.
5 *Ibid.,* p. 59.
6 *Athenaeum* (London), 3 October 1846, p. 1019.
7 *Occasional Notes etc.,* **2**, 1947, p. 65.
8 Quoted in *Occasional Motes etc.,* **2**, 1947, p. 65.
9 *History of the Royal Astronomical Society,* London, 1923, p. 9.
10 *Occasional Notes etc.,* **2**, 1947, p. 70.
11 *Ibid.,* **2**, p. 73.

CHAPTER VII

1 *Philosophical Transactions,* **35**, p. 637f.
2 J. Delambre, *Histoire de l'Astronomie au* 18 *siècle,* Paris, 1827, p. 420.
3 R. van der R. Woolley, *Quarterly Journal of the Royal Astronomical Society,* **4**, (1963), p. 52.
4 Quoted by H. W. Maunder, *The Royal Observatory,* London, 1900, p. 100.
5 W. Airy (ed.), *Autobiography of Sir George Airy,* Cambridge 1896, p. 128.
6 *Ibid.,* p. 29.
7 *Ibid.,* p. 129.
8 Quoted by Spencer Jones, *The Royal Observatory, Greenwich,* London, 1943, p. 23.
9 W. Airy, *op. cit.,* p. 241.
10 Agnes Clerke, *A Popular History of Astronomy during the Nineteenth Century,* London, 1893, p. 490.
11 *Observatory,* **5**, 1881, p. 354.
12 Spencer Jones, *op. cit.,* p. 20.

CHAPTER VIII

1   R. S. Ball, *Great Astronomers*, London, 1895, p. 238.
2   C. E. Mills and C. F. Brooke, *A Sketch Life of Sir William Huggins, K.C.B., O.M.*, London (privately printed), 1936, p. 23.
3   *Ibid.*, p. 25.
4   W. Huggins, *Publications of Sir William Huggins's Observatory*, London, 1899, **I** p. 9.
5   C. E. Mills and C. F. Brooke, *op. cit.*, p. 35.
6   *Ibid.*, pp. 59, 60.
7   E. W. Maunder, *The Royal Observatory*, London, 1900, p. 272.
8   From a copy in the possession of the Christie family.

CHAPTER IX

1   H. N. Lockyer, *Meteoric Hypothesis*, London, 1890, p. 380.
2   A. S. Eddington, *Report on the Relativity Theory of Gravitation*, London, 1918, preface.
3   Quoted by V. Douglas, *Arthur Stanley Eddington*, Edinburgh, 1956, p. 40.
4   *Ibid.*, p. 44.
5   *Ibid.*, p. 60.
6   *Ibid.*, p. 40.
7   M. Wilson, *Ninth Astronomer Royal*, Cambridge, 1951, p. 200.
8   A. Hunter, *Journal of the British Astronomical Association*, **69**, 1959, p. 7.
9   Spencer Jones, *The Royal Observatory, Greenwich*, London, 1943, p. 44.
10 A. Hunter, *op. cit.*, p. 8.

CHAPTER X

1   *Observatory*, **68**, (1948) p. 178.
2   *Monthly Notices of the Royal Astronomical Society*, **117**, (1957) p. 277.
3   J. H. Jeans, *The Universe Around Us*, Cambridge, 1929, p. 332.

Books for Further Reading

FOR THE GENERAL READER

Bonner, W. *The Mystery of the Expanding Universe,* London, 1964, Eyre & Spottiswode.

Hoyle, Fred. *Astronomy,* London, 1962. Macdonald.

Lovell, Sir B. *The Exploration of Outer Space,* London, 1962, Oxford University Press.

Moore, Patrick. *Astronomy,* London, 1964, Oldbourne.
Guide to the Stars, London, 1960, Eyre & Spottiswoode.

Motz L. and Duveen, A. *Essentials of Astronomy,* London, 1966, Blackie.

Ronan, Colin A. *Optical Astronomy,* London, 1964, Phoenix House.

Rudaux, L. and de Vaucouleurs, G. *Larousse Encyclopaedia of Astronomy,* London, 1966, Hamlyn.

Smith, F. Graham. *Radio Astronomy,* Harmondsworth, 1960, Pelican (A. 479).

Abetti, G. *A History of Astronomy,* London, 1964, Sidgwick & Jackson.

Andrade, E. N. da C. *Isaac Newton,* London, 1950, Max Parrish.

Armitage, A. *Edmond Halley,* London, 1966, Nelson.
William Herschel, London, 1962, Nelson.

Ronan, Colin A. *The Astronomers,* London, 1964, Evans.
The Ages of Science, London, 1966, Harrap.

FOR THE SPECIALIST READER

Bondi, H. *Cosmology,* London, 1961, Cambridge University Press.

Hoyle, Fred. *Galaxies, Nuclei and Quasars,* London, 1966, Heinemann.

Sciama, D. W. *The Unity of the Universe,* New York, 1959, Doubleday.

Crombie, A. C. *From Augustine to Galileo,* London, 1952, Falcon Educational Books.

Dingle, H. *The Scientific Adventure,* London, 1952, Pitman.

Douglas, Vibert. *Arthur Stanley Eddington,* London, 1956, Nelson.

Grosser, M. *The Discovery of Neptune,* Harvard, 1962, Harvard University Press.

Hoskin, M. A. *William Herschel and the Construction of the Heavens,* London, 1963, Oldbourne.

Johnson, F. R. *Astronomical Thought in Renaissance England,* Baltimore, 1932, Johns Hopkins University Press, and London, 1932, Oxford University Press.

King, H. C. *History of the Telescope,* London, 1955, Griffin.

More, L. T. *Isaac Newton,* New York, 1934, Scribner & 1962, Dover.

Pannekoek, A. *A History of Astronomy,* London, 1961, Allen & Unwin.

Ronan, Colin A. *Changing Views of the Universe,* London, 1961, Eyre & Spottiswoode.

Woolf, H. *Transits of Venus,* Princeton, 1959, Princeton University Press.

Index